365

TRAVEL
Games & Activities

Contributing Writers:
Stan and Shea Zukowski

Illustrators:
Terri and Joe Chicko

Publications International, Ltd.

Stan Zukowski is On-Line Editor for *Backpacker* magazine, where he creates and manages a Web site dedi-
cated to wilderness travel, puzzles, games, and contests
for children. He has served as the Associate Editor for
Bicycling magazine and was Editor at the Children's
Better Health Institute, which publishes seven national
children's magazines, including *Jack & Jill*, *Child Life*,
and *Children's Digest*.

Shea Zukowski is a freelance writer and a full-time
mother. She holds a B.A. in English from Ball State
University.

Illustrations: Terri and Joe Chicko
Cover Photography: Brian Warling
Models: Cameron Nyquist, Katie Otte
            Royal Model Management
Stylist: Danita Wiecek
Hair/Makeup: Nea Grapsas

CONTENTS

INTRODUCTION

Vacations—and travel in general—present a special opportunity for parents and their children to strengthen family bonds, create fond memories of happy times spent together, and simply enjoy each other's company in an atmosphere free from daily pressures and responsibilities

That's the idea, anyway. As we all know, vacations are rarely if ever without a complication or two—an unexpected delay, a sudden change in plans, not to mention long stretches of confinement in cars, planes, trains, or what have you. Being prepared to make the best of these idle times is essential, particularly if you're traveling with the troops. Even under the best of circumstances, kids will be kids, which means it won't be long before they (like the rest of us) become bored, restless, grumpy, or some dreadful combination of the above.

One way to keep the crew content is to make sure they have plenty of opportunities to keep themselves occupied, and this hefty collection of games and activities will certainly help do that. Best of all, no batteries are required!

Unlike many books of this type, however, *365 Travel Games & Activities* is designed to be more than a series of frivolous diversions, though there are plenty of those as well. Many of the activities are educational, in addition to being entertaining. Others foster group participation in a way that contributes to family unity. Still others stimulate the imagination, encouraging creative thinking. Indeed, there is something here for everyone—parents and children, boys and girls, single- and multiple-child households.

In particular, note the Parent and Single-Child icons that appear throughout the

Single-Child icon   **Parent icon**

book. The Parent icon is used to identify games and activities that either require or may benefit from adult participation. The Single-Child icon identifies activities that an individual child can enjoy alone.

The book is divided into nine chapters. There's also a handy index to help locate games easily, as well as a four-page answer section for quizzes and puzzles that require specific solutions.

Chapter 1 (Getting Ready To Go) involves making items—everything from game boards and tote bags to snacks—that kids can take with them on the trip. Be sure to skim this chapter well in advance of your departure date, allowing time to acquire materials for the projects you want to complete.

Chapter 2 (Observation Games) contains games of analysis of various kinds. Some involve common objects (license plates, billboards, highway signs, etc.) that appear continuously as you travel. Others require youngsters to study people that they come into contact with. Still others are presented as drawings, which an artist has filled with visual tricks.

Chapter 3 (Arts & Crafts) offers a wide-ranging selection of arts and crafts projects. Here, kids will find instructions for making things to play with, things to wear, things to hang up as art, practical things that can be used on the trip, and even a few silly things that are guaranteed to get a laugh. As with Chapter 1, see what materials are needed before you leave home.

Chapter 4 (Imagination Games) offers youngsters a chance to design a castle, make up stories, travel into the future, or imagine what it's like to be a bird. In this section, there are no wrong answers, and just about anything is possible.

Chapter 5 (Break-Time Games) presents games and other activities for three common, but very different, travel settings: rest stops, restaurants, and hotels. Rest stops are perfect for noisier, more physically demanding games, while restaurants are ideal for quieter,

low-impact activities. In hotels, the possibilities range from traditional board games and scavenger hunts to simple storytelling in the dark.

Chapter 6 (Mazes & Puzzles) will appeal to all who enjoy a mental challenge. Included are classic brainteasers, simple word puzzles, riddles of all kinds, question-and-answer games, and similar exercises that, while they are designed to be fun, also test one's ability to solve problems.

Chapter 7 (Word Games & Trivia) combines trivia quizzes and word games. Quizzes give youngsters a chance to show off their knowledge of popular subjects, at the same time presenting them with exciting facts that they weren't aware of. Word games combine fun and learning in a similar way.

Chapter 8 (Odds & Ends) features all kinds of games and activities that, for one reason or another, don't quite fit under the other chapter headings. The list includes card games, sing-alongs, magic tricks, and numbers games.

Chapter 9 (When You Get Home) helps keep vacation memories alive with a variety of creative projects. Most involve making things from items collected during the trip—flowers, seashells, brochures, postcards, and so on. Skim this section before you go so you'll know what materials to look for.

GETTING READY TO GO

Most of the activities in this chapter involve making things that you can take with you and have fun with while you travel. All of these items are easy to make (though some will require a little help from an adult), but a few of them call for the use of certain tools and materials that may be difficult—or impractical—to find once you leave home. For that reason, it is recommended that parents and children alike take the time to go over this chapter at least two weeks before your trip. That will give everyone plenty of time to gather everything that is needed.

SPINNER

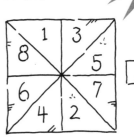

Make this handy game piece to use instead of dice for several of the games in this book.

You Will Need: 2 pieces of thin cardboard (one 4×4 inches; one ½×3 inches), 1 brad, scissors, ruler (for drawing straight lines), crayons or markers

Draw straight lines on the square piece of cardboard, and number them as shown (Picture 1). Color the triangles if you wish. Cut out an arrow at one end of the smaller piece of cardboard. Attach the arrow to your spinner by poking the brad through the arrow piece and then through the center of the numbered board (Picture 2). Flatten the arms of the brad against the back of your spinner, and you're set to play. To spin, flick the arrow with your finger.

Picture 1

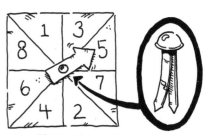

Picture 2

FRUIT LEATHER

Fruit leather is a tasty treat that is easy to make a few days before you travel. Are you ready to be a candy chef?

You Will Need: 4 or 5 pieces fresh fruit (peaches and apricots seem to work best), 2 tablespoons honey, ½ teaspoon lemon juice, blender, 1-quart pot, cookie sheet, spoon, waxed paper. You will also need a parent or another adult to help you.

Lay a large piece of waxed paper on a cookie sheet. Have a grown-up boil a pot of water and then carefully put the fruit in it; boil for 1 minute, then drain the water. Next, run the fruit under cold water, then rub each one gently to remove the skin. Cut the fruit into small pieces, which you will put into a blender with the remaining ingredients. Blend until very smooth. Pour this mixture into the 1-quart pot. Carefully bring to a boil until it is very thick, stirring constantly so it doesn't burn.

Finally, spread the mixture on the waxed paper so it's about ¼ inch thick. Let it sit on the counter until it is dry (3 or 4 days). Enjoy!

CALIFORNIA OR BUST!

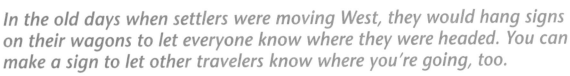

In the old days when settlers were moving West, they would hang signs on their wagons to let everyone know where they were headed. You can make a sign to let other travelers know where you're going, too.

You Will Need: 1 piece of light cardboard about 8 inches square, markers or crayons, glue stick, scissors, old magazines

On the cardboard, write the name of the state or city you will be visiting and put "or Bust!" beneath it. Decorate your sign with markers, crayons, or pictures you cut out of magazines. If you are traveling in a different state, make a sign that says, "Wave if you're from" and then put the name of your home state underneath. Keep count of how many people wave to you.

BACKSEAT TOTE

4

When you're riding in the back of the car, it's easy to lose things under the front seat or between the cushions. Make this crazy travel tote to keep your stuff in one place.

You Will Need: 1 pair old pants with belt loops, 2 feet of rope (or cord or heavy string), scissors, needle and thread (or sewing machine), fabric paint or permanent markers (optional). Ask mom or dad for help before you begin.

Cut the legs off the pants (Picture 1). With a sewing machine or needle and thread, sew the legs of the pants shut (Picture 2). Tie one end of the rope to a belt loop on the left side of the pants. Tie the other end of the rope to a belt loop on the right side of the pants (Picture 3). Hook the rope over the back of the headrest of the driver's seat or passenger seat (Picture 4). Use your travel tote to hold books, magazines, notepads, gorp, or whatever you want. The pants pockets are perfect for small items such as coins and pens. You can even take your travel tote with you as a carryall. Decorate it with fabric paint or markers.

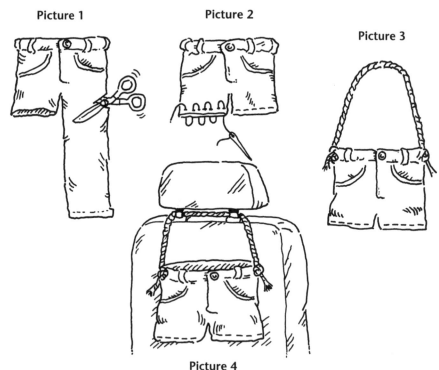

Picture 1

Picture 2

Picture 3

Picture 4

TRAVEL TRIVIA
Some Texans like to brag about how big their state is, but Alaska is a lot bigger. In fact, if Alaska were cut in half, each half would still be bigger than Texas.

CHARM BAG

5

Charm bags hold small objects that bring good luck or happy memories. Make your own, and you'll have a private place for all the cool stuff you find, such as coins, rocks, four-leaf clovers, and so on.

You Will Need: 1 piece of cloth or felt (4×12 inches), 1 piece of string or cord (at least 10 inches long), needle and thread (or sewing machine). Ask mom or dad for help.

Fold the short end of the cloth down 1 inch, making a flap (Picture 1). Sew the flap to the cloth about ½ inch from the edge. Leave the ends open (Picture 2). Follow the same steps for the other end of the cloth. This makes 2 "tubes" at opposite ends of the cloth (Picture 3). Later you will put your string through these tubes to make a drawstring. Next, fold the cloth in half. If the cloth has a pattern, fold so the pattern is on the inside (Picture 4). Sew the sides of the cloth together, about ½ inch in from the edge. Stop sewing before you reach the tubes (Picture 5). Now turn your charm bag inside out. Push the string through both tubes and tie the ends of the string together (Picture 6).

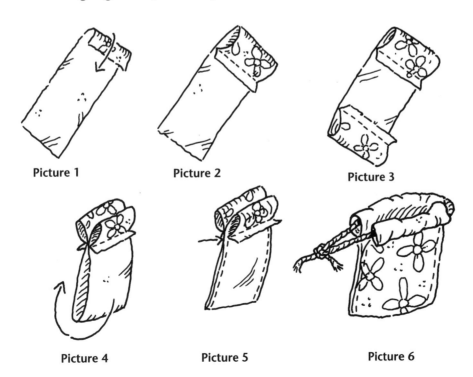

Picture 1   Picture 2   Picture 3

Picture 4   Picture 5   Picture 6

GAME BOARD BOOK

6

With this do-it-yourself book, you can take your favorite board games along when you travel—and they'll take up less space than a notebook!

You Will Need: Large pieces (10×12 inches) heavy felt for game boards (the number of pieces depends on the number of games you want to make), felt scrap pieces (for game pieces), 1 piece (10×12 inches) of heavy cardboard, 1 zipper-lock plastic baggy, white glue, clear tape, scissors, permanent markers or fabric paint

Copy the design of your favorite game boards onto the pieces of heavy felt using markers or fabric paint. Leave a 1-inch strip of blank space on the left side of each board so you can join them together as a book. Then cut out enough felt pieces so you can play each game you choose to make. Here are some popular game boards you can make:

Reverse It (see #201) can be played on a standard checkerboard (8 rows of 8 squares), but you need 64 playing pieces—one for every square. Each piece should be white on one side, black on the other.

Checkers and **Chess** use the same game board (8 rows of 8 squares) but have different playing pieces. To play Checkers, which requires 24 pieces (12 for each player), you can use the black and white pieces from the Reverse It game. (See At the Hotel in Chapter 5 for different Checkers games you can play.) Chess needs its own special pieces: 16 for each player, 2 colors. Write the name of each piece on one side or draw a picture to show which piece is which.

Tic-Tac-Toe and **Tic-Tac-Toe-Tee** (See #304 for rules on how to play.) boards are easy to make. Use the Checkers and Reverse It markers.

After all your boards are finished, glue them together along the left side like the pages of a book. Then turn the whole thing over, and glue the cardboard to the back of the last board. This makes the book stiff enough to play on. You can add new boards at any time by gluing them to the top of the stack. Finally, tape the zipper-lock baggy to the cardboard. Use it to store the felt pieces you make for each game.

MAKE YOUR CLAIM

7

Make the cards for this great observation game before you leave on your trip. You can store them in your Backseat Tote (see #4).

You Will Need: 30 to 50 index cards, old magazines and catalogs, scissors, glue or glue stick

Think about your trip. Make a list of common, everyday things you might see while you travel. Here are some examples. **Things:** police cars, office buildings, trees, soda machines, lounge chairs, tractors, jet airplanes. **People:** waitpersons, police officers, firefighters, lifeguards, cashiers. **Animals:** dogs, cats, cows, horses, monkeys, elephants, bears.

Look through old magazines and catalogs. Cut out the pictures of the people and things you think you will see probably see. Use your list to help you remember. Glue 1 picture to each index card. To play the I Claim It! game, see #70. For the most fun, make at least 30 cards with as many different pictures as you can find.

MAKE A TANGRAM

8

Tangram Pattern

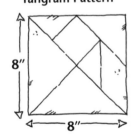

8"

8"

A tangram is like a recyclable puzzle, because you can make so many shapes and patterns with it. Here's one you can keep in your Travel Supply Box (#12). For games you can play with your tangram, see #325.

You Will Need: One 8×8-inch sheet of light cardboard, ruler, scissors, pencil

Sample Tangrams

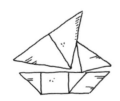

Look closely at the pattern in the accompanying picture. Use your ruler and pencil to draw the same pattern onto your sheet of light cardboard, then use scissors to cut out the pieces. You can decorate your tangram in many different ways—color each piece a different color, create different patterns on each one, or whatever you like. NOTE: It is easier to color or decorate your tangram puzzle before you cut it out.

MAKE A KNITTING FRAME

Here's a knitting project that needs no needles.

You Will Need: 1 small square piece of wood (3×3 inches and at least 1 inch thick), 4 nails (½-inch), hammer, drill, sandpaper, knitting yarn

Have mom or dad help you drill a hole in the center of your block of wood. Make it big enough for you to put a large pencil through easily. Next, hammer 4 nails about halfway into the block, as shown. Use sandpaper to smooth the edges of the hole so your yarn doesn't get snagged. Hold the frame so that the nails are pointing up at you. Start by pushing the end of your yarn down through the bottom of the hole. Moving counterclockwise, wrap your yarn once around each nail.

When you get to where you started, wrap the yarn around the first nail again. You now have 2 loops of yarn wrapped around the nail. Carefully pick up the bottom loop of yarn and pull it over the top loop, then slip the bottom loop completely off the nail. Grab the end of your yarn and tug on it gently before moving on to the next nail and repeating the same steps. As you continue moving from nail to nail, you'll see a long knitted chain appearing from the hole in the bottom of your block.

There are many things you can do with your chains when you get home. You can use them to decorate the doorway to your room, for example, or try making a drink coaster by wrapping your chain into a spiral and gluing it onto a piece of cardboard.

TRAVEL TRIVIA

Although it ranks third in size among the 50 states (only Alaska and Texas are bigger), California is number one in population (26 million). It also has a larger economy, grows more food, and has more cars and highways than any other state.

MAKE AN AUTOGRAPH BOOK

10

Meet interesting people on your trip, and play a game at the same time!

You Will Need: Decorating materials (old photos, magazines, tissue paper, fabric, construction paper, markers, crayons), school-sized spiral notebook, glue or glue stick, scissors

Write "Autograph Book" and your name in fancy letters on the front cover of the notebook. Decorate the covers with your choice of designs and materials. At the top of each page inside, write one of the words from our list. These are the people whose autographs you will try to get. Try to think of other people you might meet when you are with your mom or dad. One page, for example, might be for "Waitresses and Waiters." On that page, collect autographs of the people who serve you and your family in restaurants. If you want, you can play for points. Next to every person below is a number. Score that amount for every autograph you get from that kind of person. If you get three police officers' autographs, you get 30 points.

Cashiers—3 points
Family friends—3 points
Grandma/Grandpa—3 points
Hotel clerks—5 points
Lifeguards—10 points
Mom/Dad—1 point
Police officers—10 points
Sister/Brother—1 point
Theme park characters—20 points
Uncles/Aunts—3 points
Waiters/Waitresses—3 points

MAP YOUR ROUTE

Getting where you're going is even more fun if you know how to get there. Help plan your family's driving route. You can also figure out how many miles you will travel.

You Will Need: Map(s) of the state(s) you'll be traveling through, highlighting markers, ruler, paper, pencil

Find your hometown and the city you'll be visiting (if this is several states away, you may need to look at a national map). Look for the thickest road lines that come closest to these two places. These lines show you where the interstate highways are. They're often blue or red in color. If the highways don't go directly through your home or visiting city, find smaller roads that will get you there. Use markers to highlight the path you'll take. When you're done finding roads between the two places, ask mom or dad to show you which route you'll be taking. Did your route match theirs?

Now go back and measure the distance between the two places. Usually there will be a small bar on one of the corners of your map that shows you how many miles equal 1 inch on the map. This is called the map's scale. Using your ruler, count how many inches between your starting and stopping places. Multiply this number by the number of miles per inch. If the scale says "20 miles = 1 inch" and you measure 5 inches, then the distance is 100 miles, because 5 times 20 is 100.

TRAVEL SUPPLY BOX

This special box is perfect for carrying all the games, crafts, pencils, crayons, and paper that you want to take on your trip.

You Will Need: Shoe box, glue stick, scissors, decorating materials (old travel magazines, fabric, different types of paper, markers, stickers)

Let your imagination run wild. Because this is a travel box, think about using pictures of cars, planes, and boats. If you are going someplace you've never visited, try to find pictures about that place and use them as decorations.

CAR GORP

13

Hikers love "gorp"—a type of trail snack—because it's easy to make and fun to eat. You'll love it because you get to invent your own recipe!

You Will Need: ½ cup unsalted peanuts or almonds, ½ cup raisins, ½ cup of your favorite dry cereal, ½ cup of M&Ms, plus your choice of any other dry snack ingredients, including dried apricots, dried apples, jelly beans, pretzel sticks, crackers (Don't use chocolates or other snacks that can melt and become gooey.)

Put all of the ingredients into an airtight container, such as a large sealable sandwich bag or a plastic bowl with a lid. Shake well to mix them together. Keep the container with you in the car, and have a snack now and then on your trip.

TRIP DIARY

14

This diary is a collection of your dreams and memories.

You Will Need: Notebook, pen or pencil

If you keep a diary, you can recall all of the fun and exciting things you did on your vacation any time you want to. Set aside some time before you travel to think about what you hope will happen on your trip. Make a list in your diary of things to check off once you're on the road.

If you want, you can also make a fill-in-the-blank entry of things you want to remember, such as:

The most delicious meal I ate was_____.
The funniest thing that happened was_____.
The most exciting thing that happened was_____.

And so on. Then you'll have a head start on writing once your trip has started. Be sure and jot down any surprises that happen along the way!

UP PERISCOPE!

Pretend you're on a submarine with this milk-carton periscope. You can look through the window or around corners, and nobody will know you're there!

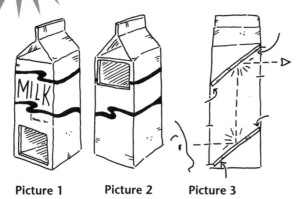

Picture 1   Picture 2   Picture 3

You Will Need: Empty 1-quart milk carton (clean and dry), 2 small mirrors (pocket mirrors or makeup mirrors), scissors, clear tape. You may want to ask your mom or dad for help on this project.

Cut a hole in the milk carton on one side near the bottom (Picture 1). It should be almost as wide as the carton and 2 inches tall. Cut another hole in the milk carton, this time on the other side near the top (Picture 2). Make it the same size as the first hole. The next part is a little tricky: Tape the mirrors inside the milk carton with the mirrored sides facing out, one at the top, and one at the bottom (Picture 3). Angle them as shown in the picture. By looking in through the bottom hole, you will see through both mirrors and out the top.

YOU KNOW IT

Make yourself an "expert" for your next trip by finding out as much as you can about your destination before you go.

You Will Need: Encyclopedias, travel guides, brochures

Once you know where you'll be traveling, make yourself the family expert by learning as much as you can about that place—local history, major attractions, fun places to eat, and so on. If you'll be visiting a large city, have your mom or dad call the Convention & Visitors Bureau to get information about special events and things to see and do while you are there. State tourist boards are a good source as well. So is your local library. In addition to encyclopedias, you will want to look through travel books covering the area you'll be visiting.

MAKE A FLOWER PRESS

Flowers you collect can be used to make all kinds of lovely crafts.

Picture 1

Picture 2

You Will Need: 2 pieces of plywood (8×8 inches), 6 pieces of corrugated cardboard (8×8 inches), 6 paper towel pieces (8×8 inches), 4 bolts (3 inches long), 4 wing nuts, drill

Ask mom or dad to drill a hole in each corner of one plywood square (Picture 1). Have mom or dad lay this square on top of the other square and drill through the holes again so both sets of holes match up. You can trim the corners off the cardboard and paper towels so they don't cover the holes in the boards (Picture 2).

Picture 3

Arrange the cardboard and paper towel pieces between the 2 boards in this order: cardboard, 2 paper towel pieces, cardboard, 2 paper towel pieces, and so on. Place the flowers you want to press between the paper towel pieces. Insert the bolts in each corner and tighten all the wing nuts to squeeze the flowers as much as possible (Picture 3). Leave the flowers in the press for at least 2 weeks so they dry properly.

FLASH

Can you outthink your opponent? Make this game ahead of time, and take it with you when you go on your trip.

You Will Need: 20 to 30 index cards cut in half, 1 sheet of scrap paper, pen

On scrap paper, make a list of categories. Make the categories as specific as possible. For example, instead of writing down BIRDS as a category, you can get 4 categories by writing SEA BIRDS, JUNGLE BIRDS, FOREST BIRDS, and CITY BIRDS. When you have a list of 40 to 60 different categories, write one on each piece of index card. Shuffle the pieces together like a deck of cards. Now you're ready to play!

Pick a person to turn over the cards. The first person to call out an item from the category written on the card gets to keep the card. When the deck is gone, the person with the most cards wins the round. Shuffle the cards and start again.

Here's a list of possible categories to get you started: zoo animals, jungle animals, farm animals, planets, cars, sports, snack foods, sodas, cereals, cartoons, movies, movie stars, book titles, colors, trees, flowers.

19

TREASURE HUNT

The world is full of treasures if you know where to look!

Treasure Hunt is a game that really keeps you hopping. Before you leave on a trip, make a list of secret treasures to find while you're traveling. Make sure the treasures will be small enough to fit into a shoe box.

When you leave on your trip, be on the lookout for the items on your list. Check them off one by one as you find them. We started you off with a sample list. What other treasures can you think to find?

Business card with the name "Sam" or "Sally" on it
Feather
Amusement park ticket stub
Paper menu
Penny you found on the beach, ground, or street
Rock with 3 different colors in it
Seashell
Toothpick with colored streamers on it
Yellow flower

RECYCLER GAME BOARD

20

Here's a game board that's easy to make, fits in your shirt pocket, and sets up differently every time you play.

You Will Need: Enough thin cardboard or heavy paper to cut into 30 squares (2 inches each), scissors, markers or crayons

Write "Start" on 1 card, "Finish" on 1 card, "Go Back 1 Space" on 5 cards, "Go Ahead 1 Space" on 5 cards, "Lose 1 Turn" on 1 card, "Take Another Turn" on 1 card, and "Go Back To Start" on 1 card. Next, make 2 cards for each of the following instructions: "Go Ahead 2 Spaces," "Go Back 2 Spaces," "Go Ahead 3 Spaces," and "Go Back 3 Spaces." Leave 7 cards blank, or draw silly pictures on them for fun. (If you have paper left over, you can make more 2-inch squares, but leave them blank.)

For instructions on how to play Recycler, see #197 in Chapter 5.

OBSERVATION GAMES

Games of observation can take many forms. Some make use of common objects—license plates, cars, billboards, and highway signs—that are found everywhere around us. Others are presented as drawings, which an artist has filled with visual tricks and hidden items. Still others require you to study people, be they family members or complete strangers. A few of the games rely on your ability to observe certain sounds. As different as the games in this chapter are, most of them require no special materials beyond paper and pencil.

ARTIST!

You'd better be quick on the draw to do well in this game.

You Will Need: Watch, paper, pencil, a cup or hat

Before you begin, ask someone who won't be playing with you to write down some parts of songs or famous sayings. Have the person write each one on a small, separate piece of paper and then fold it. Put these pieces of paper into a cup or hat. If younger kids are playing, you can write down names of animals or objects that they can draw instead of songs or sayings.

The first player chooses a piece of paper from the cup. Then he or she draws clues on the paper so the other players can guess what the phrase is. Of course, you can't use letters or numbers—that would be spelling, not drawing!

You'd better be quick on the draw; you only have 2 minutes to get your point across. If someone guesses your word or phrase in that time, you get 1 point. If not, you get no points. Either way, it's someone else's turn to be the Artist.

22

MAD ADS

Be on the lookout for different ads to see who has the best eagle eye!

Advertisements are all around you—sometimes on the road, on other cars, on buildings, on the radio, and even in the sky! This is a simple game you can play with 1 or more people.

First, you need to decide what type of ads you'll be looking for (food ads, ads for hotels, and so on). Then you need to decide how many points each type of advertising is worth (for example, 1 point for a billboard ad, 2 points for a radio ad, 3 points for a passing truck, and so on). Once you've decided what you're looking for and how much all are worth, be on the lookout for all the ads you can find. The first one to spot an ad and point it out gets the points for that ad. One ad per person. Play as long as you want. The person who gets the highest score wins.

CAR COLLECTING

23

Can you spot your dream car? Make it yours!

Almost everybody has a favorite car or truck. Some people like Corvettes. Other people like Porsches or Monster Trucks. If you've never thought much about cars, here's an easy way to start. Just pick a type of car you think is cool, and count how many of them you see on the road.

How quickly can you spot your dream car? Usually you will just read the name as it passes you. But many cars look alike today, so take a second look. How big is your dream car? What does the grille (the front of the car) look like? Is there a special hood ornament? Don't forget to look for special features on the back of the car, too. Soon you'll be able to recognize your dream car from far away. Don't forget to keep track of how many you see when you're driving around!

CRAZY CARAVAN

Get ready to switch gears—and count as fast as you can!

Each player chooses a type of vehicle (van, truck, or car) to count. Let's say you pick cars. On "Go," count how many cars pass by, scoring 1 point for each. Other players count trucks or vans. The first person to get to 50 wins.

But wait a minute, you say. There are more cars on the road than trucks or vans, so the person who picks cars will always win! That's true, but we're not done with the rules yet! Watch out for red cars. They don't count for points, but every time you pass by a red car (or a red car passes you), players switch the kind of vehicle they're counting, moving left to right. You'll be counting cars one minute, vans the next, and trucks right after that.

An interesting variation to this game is to assign different point values to each type of vehicle: 1 point for cars, 2 points for vans, and 3 points for trucks—or even 1 point for cars, 3 for vans, and 5 for trucks. Talk about switching gears!

BIG & SMALL

No matter where you go, keep your eyes open for the biggest and smallest things.

You can play this observation game with 1 or more players. The object is to find the biggest and smallest thing in every category you can think of: cars, trucks, buildings, people, animals, houses, road signs, and so on.

Whoever sees the biggest or smallest object calls it out. "Biggest car, right over there!" Then the challenge is to find something even bigger (or smaller) in that category.

WORD HUNT

26

If you have a favorite letter, here is a game for you!

Each player is on a hunt, tracking down all the things that begin with a certain letter—such as Road, Restaurant, Redwood tree, and Red light. If you're playing with more than 1 person, each person can either choose a different letter, or race each other to find the most words using the same letter.

Don't forget synonyms! Synonyms are different words that have the same meaning. For example, it would be good to spot a car if you're looking for "C" words, but a car would also count for "A" words (automobile) or "V" words (vehicle) depending on what you called it.

CITY SAFARI

27

Next time you're walking around a city, or just stuck in heavy downtown traffic, look up for a big surprise!

If you're in a downtown area, you'll see plenty of cars, people, and buildings all around you. But if you know where to look, you just might find a whole zoo of silent animals watching you. Buildings that are very old are often decorated with little carvings and statues of animals and people—and sometimes monsters called gargoyles. How many different animals, faces, and creatures can you find? Imagine what it would be like to see the city from where they are, high above the street.

Buildings aren't the only places to find stone animals and other creatures. Look on monuments, fountains, old fences, and tombstones. If you have a camera, take photos of the animals you find on your city safari, and save them in their very own book.

ONE, TWO, THREE . . .

The fastest way to 10 in this game is through teamwork!

Players count from 1 to 10 by finding different numbers of objects. For example, someone might call out, "I see ONE dog by that tree." Someone else might say, "I see TWO flags flying in that parking lot," and then, "I see THREE mailboxes by that apartment building," followed by, "I see FOUR shopping carts outside that store," and so on to 10 objects. Players must count in order from 1 to 10.

I SPY IN COLOR

A quick and simple game you can play just about anywhere.

Pick someone to be the Spy. The Spy looks around and secretly chooses an object. (Just be sure it's something that all the other players can see.) After choosing an object, the Spy says: "I spy with my eye something that is the color _____." For example, if the object is a red apple, you would add the word "red" to the end of the rhyme. The other players take turns trying to guess the object you've chosen. The first player to guess correctly becomes the Spy.

I SPY RHYME

Test your rhyming skills with a more challenging version of this popular observation game.

This is another way to play I Spy. The basic rules are the same, but instead of giving color clues, you give the other players a word that rhymes with the secret thing you see. Let's say that the Spy is thinking of the word DOG. He or she would say, "I spy with my eye something that rhymes with FOG."

Of course, the Spy can give a tricky clue if he or she wants to. How? Well, POOCH is another name for DOG, right? To be tricky, the Spy could say, "I spy with my little eye something that rhymes with SMOOCH." Clever, huh? Before making rhymes, try to think of a less-common word for the object you're thinking of.

NAME GAME

You can find your name on a billboard sign—if you know where to look!

To win, be the first person to spell out your name by finding the letters on billboard signs. There are only 3 rules: You must find the letters in the order they appear in your name (In other words, you can't pick and choose letters as they come along); a sign may be used only once, and for only 1 letter (Once somebody calls out a letter, nobody else can use that sign again, including the person who called it out); and to be fair, make sure all players have the same number of letters in their names. If Andrew and Lisa are playing, for example, shorten Andrew's name to Andy, or add part of Lisa's middle name to her first name to make it as long as Andrew. If that doesn't work, try spelling other people's names—presidents, movie stars, favorite athletes, cartoon characters, and so on.

LIP READING

Just because mom or dad asks you to be quiet doesn't mean you can't talk to each other—silently!

Many people with hearing difficulties use both sign language and lip reading to communicate with other people. To learn sign language, you will need a special teacher. But you can practice lip reading anytime, anywhere, as long as you have a partner. Start by mouthing (saying silently) one word, such as "tomato," as someone else tries to figure out the word you are saying.

Make your mouth, lip, and face movements bigger than normal. This will help the other person understand more quickly. Facial expressions are good, too. For example, if the word is "happy," then put a happy look on your face as you say it.

Now have the other person mouth a word, and YOU try to guess. Don't watch the person's eyes. Instead, watch the shapes that his or her lips, mouth, and tongue make when they say the word. How quickly can you guess the word? Move up to mouthing more words, and finally, whole sentences.

CHANCE

Keep your fingers crossed, and hope the right cars pass by!

The object of this game is to count to 9 by watching the license plates of other cars. Let's run through a sample game: Choose who goes first. On "Go," Player 1 watches the license plate of the next car that you pass, or that passes you. If the number 1 is on that car's license plate, Player 1 scores 1 point and gets to look again on the next car for the number 2, then the number 3, and so on. Play continues until Player 1 misses—that is, until he or she can't find the correct number on the next license plate.

When Player 1 misses, Player 2 gets to play, starting with whatever number Player 1 ended on. Players score 1 point for every number they spot in order when it is their turn. When the last player spots the number 9, the game is over. The player with the most points wins.

GREAT DETECTIVE

Sherlock Holmes, the great detective, was a man who noticed every little detail. Can you be a Sherlock, too?

The rules of this game are simple, but the challenges can get tricky pretty fast. Basically, 2 people study each other very carefully, making a mental note of every detail: how the other person's hair is combed, color and position of clothing, type of shoes worn, and so on. Then, one player at a time closes his or her eyes (or leaves the room) while the other player makes some small change in appearance—such as untying a shoe, rolling up one sleeve, or turning a hat slightly. The other person must then guess what's different. The player who can do it in the fewest guesses wins. If the game is played in a hotel room or restaurant, players can move or alter objects.

ZANY NATIONAL PARK

The drawing on the opposite page is really 3 puzzles in 1. Test your powers of observation by completing the following activities. (Answers on page 233.)

First, try to find 5 things that begin with the letter P.

Now find 5 things that don't belong in Zany National Park. (Answers from #35 don't count!)

Can you find the 3 hidden pictures in the drawing?

TRAVEL TRIVIA

The strongest wind ever measured reached speeds of 231 miles per hour. It happened on top of New Hampshire's Mount Washington in 1935.

38

ROAD SIGN BASEBALL

It's one, two, three strikes you're out—in the ol' back seat! You can play baseball in the car, and you don't even need a bat.

Decide who will be the Batter and who will be the Pitcher. The Batter tries to score by finding special road signs, as listed below. The Pitcher tries to get the Batter "out" by spotting red-colored cars (or some other agreed upon substitute), each of which counts as 1 strike.

Here are the road signs you should watch for, as well as how many bases (points) the batter scores for spotting each one. But remember—if the pitcher sees a red car first, you get 1 strike. And as everybody knows, 3 strikes and "Yer out!" Then it's the other player's turn to bat.

Speed Limit: A single (1 point)
Stop: A single (1 point)
Exit: A single (1 point)
No U-Turn: A double (2 points)
Yield: A double (2 points)
Do Not Pass: A double (2 points)
Trucks Must Use Right Lane: A triple (3 points)
School Crossing: A triple (3 points)
Deer Crossing: A triple (3 points)
Watch For Ice On Bridge: Home Run (4 points)
Rest Stop: Home Run (4 points)
Weigh Station: Home Run (4 points)

LICENSE PLATE BINGO

This game is best for people with excellent eyesight!

Every time an out-of-state license plate is seen, the first player to spot it calls out "Bingo!" and scores 1 point. Players can also choose a certain number—such as 5—and look for it, too. An out-of-state license that reads ARB 8535, for example, would be a Bingo-Bingo-Bingo (1 Bingo for being out-of-state, and 2 Bingos for the numbers), counting for 3 points total. You don't have to keep points, but if you do, the winner is the person who gets 10 out-of-state Bingos and 10 special-number Bingos first.

ROAD-EO

Round up those cars, pardner, and git 'em all back to the corral. No matter what direction you're driving, you can always head to the Old West in this highway game.

Pick a color of a car (let's say blue). To round up all the blue cars, you must estimate (guess) how many cars of that color you will pass or will pass you in the next 5 minutes. Use a watch to keep time.

How close was your guess? If you play with another player, the winner of the Road-eo is the person whose guess is closest to the actual number of cars that pass by.

SONG-TAC-TOE

This game is sort of like Car-Tac-Toe, only you need to use your ears.

Make a Tic-Tac-Toe grid (draw 4 lines in a square so that you have 9 smaller squares inside), and write the name of a song and/or singer in each box. Then sit back and listen to the radio. Every time you hear one of the songs (or singers) that you've chosen, place an X in the appropriate box. First card to get 3 in a row wins. (HINT: If you're playing alone, see which card wins first!)

AMUSEMENT PARK

You won't need a ticket to visit the amusement park on the opposite page. Test your powers of observation by completing the following activities. (Answers on page 233.)

42 Find 5 things that don't belong in an amusement park.

43 Find 5 things that begin with the letter R.

44 Find 3 things hidden in this picture.

TRAVEL TRIVIA

Pensacola, Florida, is nicknamed the "City of Five Flags" because, over the course of its history, it has been ruled by five different nations: Spain, England, France, the Confederacy, and the United States.

45 WHAT'S WRONG IN TIME?

Take a look at this picture, and you'll see what it was like to be a kid living back in the colonial days of George Washington.

Everything here looks just like it did more than 200 years ago. But wait...how did that get in there? It seems our artist made a mistake, accidentally adding a few things that weren't even invented in 1776. How many out-of-time objects can you find? (Answers on page 233.)

HUMAN BEHAVIOR

46

The world is full of sights to see—but sometimes the most fun sights of all are other people!

Score 1 point every time you see someone doing one of the following things. Try to think of some more activities to look for as you "people-watch" on your vacation.

Crying
Biting nails
Chewing on a toothpick
Combing hair
Holding hands
Hugging
Licking the bottom of an ice cream cone
Looking through binoculars
Reading a map

Scratching nose
Shaking hands
Talking on a cellular phone
Walking with both hands in pockets
Wearing a hat backward
Wearing sneakers without socks
Wearing sunglasses on top of head
Yawning

ROADSIDE BLACKJACK

47

All you have to do is add numbers until you get to 21—or close to it—without going over! Of course, if you do get 21, you win automatically.

You can either use license plate numbers or road sign numbers, but whichever you choose, you have to stick with that choice for the rest of the game. To play, be on the lookout for the first 2 numbers you see, and call them out. Add them together. If you are close to 21 (9+9, for example, totaling 18), you might want to end your turn there. If you do, then the other player has to beat your number without going over 21. The closer you get to 21, the harder it will be for the next player to beat you.

If the sum of the two numbers was low (7+3, for example, totaling 10), you can add the first number of the next license plate or road sign number you see (just as you could ask for another card if you were playing traditional Blackjack). You can continue to add to your total this way until you decide to stop, or until you go over 21 and lose automatically.

CAR-TAC-TOE

Here's a great game you can play by yourself or with another person.

You Will Need: Paper, pencil

Make a chart like you do in Tic-Tac-Toe, but put the names of different types of cars, trucks, or motorcycles that you know inside the boxes. Then, every time you see one of the vehicles you've chosen, cross it off on the grid.

If you're playing with more than 1 person, see who can be the first to get 3 in a row. If you're playing alone, try making several cards to "race" against each other. If you want, you could make one card for cars, another one for trucks, and a third for motorcycles.

TRAVEL TRIVIA

Arizona's Grand Canyon—217 miles long and 18 miles across at its widest point—is the world's biggest canyon. The deepest (7,900 feet) is Hells Canyon, located on the Snake River between Idaho and Oregon.

CURRENCY QUIZ

You can turn paper money into hidden picture puzzles!

Can you find the following words and pictures hidden on paper money? (Answers on page 233.)

One-Dollar Bill: An old-fashioned key, 3 human eyes, 13 arrows, the Latin phrase "one" (8 times), the words "E Pluribus Unum" (which in Latin means "Out of many, one")

Five-Dollar Bill: The word "Lincoln" (2 times), the word "five" (11 times)

COLOR CHASE

Play this game while you're looking out your car window.

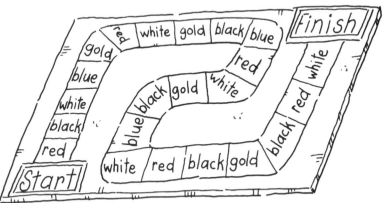

You can make the board for this game ahead of time (see #122, the Game Game). We drew a sample game, but you can make one any shape or size you like.

Each player takes turns looking out the window and calling out the color of a car that passes the vehicle. Move your finger to the next square that matches the color of the car you spotted. The first one to get to the end wins.

Can you change the rules and shape of the game to make something different?

WORD OF THE DAY

Have you ever said, "I've heard that one a million times"? That's an exaggeration for sure! But with this game you can find out how much you're REALLY hearing the same old thing.

Next time you're on vacation, pick a "word of the day" each morning. Then count how many times you hear or see that word during the day. Of course, you don't want your word to be too common—such as "the," "and," or "you"—or you'll be counting all day instead of enjoying your trip. Then again, don't make it too unusual, either—like radish or skyscraper—or you might not hear it at all.

Players can pick their own words of the day or choose one word or phrase for the whole group. (If you play as a group, it helps to have someone be the official scorekeeper.) Now, every time you hear or see your word—at the restaurant, on the radio, on a billboard—call out "word of the day!" and score 1 point.

52 SCAVENGER HUNT

Start a collection without carrying anything home!

In this no-mess scavenger hunt, watch for special sights on your trip. Every time you see something in the list below, score that many points. You can play by yourself or have a contest with other people. You can add to this list, too. Just remember that unusual things should be worth more points than common things.

Animals
Cow/2
Horse/2
Crow/3
Duck/3
Raccoon/4
Deer/4
Goat/5
Sheep/5
Bear/10
Dolphin/15

Vehicles
Motorcycle/2
Speedboat/2
Dump truck/4
Tow truck/4
Motor home/5
Antique car/5
Helicopter/6
Cement mixer/8
Hot air balloon/10
Coast Guard boat/15

People
Waiter or waitress/2
Lifeguard/2
Police officer/3
Construction worker/3
Hotel clerk/4
Ticket taker/4
Flight attendant/6
Toll booth attendant/6
Musician/10
Juggler/15

IMPERSONATIONS

53

In this game, you can be whomever you want to be—even the President of the United States!

The object of Impersonations is to act like someone else and have the other players guess who you are pretending to be. You can choose a famous movie or sports star, a family member, or someone from your neighborhood. The only rule is that you must think of someone whom everyone has heard of.

Use your face and body to act as much like that person as you can. How does that person stand, walk, or sit? What do you usually see them doing? What is something special that they do? Try playing first with the volume off (no talking). Then, if the other players want, they can say "turn on the volume," which means you can talk like that person. The player who guesses who you are gets to go next.

FACE CHARADES

Can you let everyone know how you feel—without saying anything?

This game is a lot like regular charades, but instead of acting out a word or phrase, you act out a feeling or emotion and have the other players guess what it is. This is a great game for the back of the car, where you can't move around very much.

Before you begin, have each person write 3 or 4 emotions on different pieces of paper. Fold them up and put them into a cup or hat. Each player takes a turn drawing an emotion out of the hat and then acting it out for the other players. This must be done without making any sound and without moving any part of the body except for the face and head. That's right, no hand, arm, leg, or other body motions.

The following are some feelings and emotions to start out with. How many more can you think of?

HAPPINESS	SADNESS	SHYNESS	SURPRISE
HUNGER	ANGER	LOVE	CONFUSION
FRIGHT	SLEEPINESS	DISGUST	BOREDOM

GIBBERISH CHARADES

Have you ever tried talking without saying words? Its harder than you think!

This is similar to regular charades, in which players take turns thinking of a word and then acting it out silently for other players to guess. But in Gibberish Charades, you are allowed to make a sound as long as you're not saying real words. You can make sounds, grunts, groans, and even make up fake words if you like. But if you say a real word, you're out of the game!

REST STOP

The drawing on the opposite page is really 3 puzzles in 1. Test your powers of observation by completing the following activities. (Answers on page 233.)

Find at least 5 things that begin with the letter R.

Find 5 things that are wrong with this picture.

There are 6 hidden letters in this picture. Find them, then unscramble them to form a word that describes what you have after visiting a rest stop.

TRAVEL TRIVIA
The oldest road in the United States is New Mexico's El Camino Real.
It was built in 1581.

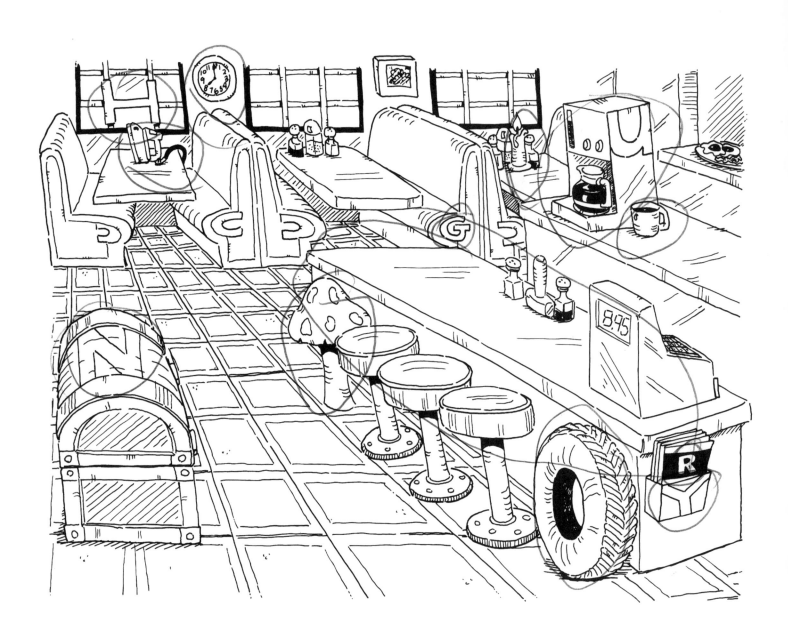

RESTAURANT SCENE

The drawing on the opposite page is really 3 puzzles in 1. Test your powers of observation by completing the following activities. (Answers on page 233.)

Find 5 things that are wrong with this picture.

Find 5 things that begin with letter C.

There are 6 hidden letters in this drawing. Find them, then unscramble them to form a word that describes the restaurant's customers.

TRAVEL TRIVIA

When George Washington was sworn in as the first President of the United States in 1789, the nation's capital was New York, then as now the country's largest city.

HOTEL POOL SCENE

The drawing on the opposite page is really 3 puzzles in 1. Test your powers of observation by completing the following activities. (Answers on page 233.)

Find 5 things that begin with the letter S.

Find 5 things that are wrong with this picture.

There are 6 letters hidden around the pool area. Find them, then unscramble them to form a word that is heard around the pool all day.

TRAVEL TRIVIA

Oregon's Crater Lake is the deepest lake in the United States. Formed by an extinct volcano, it is more than 1,900 feet deep.

MATCH IT #1

See if you can't put a little order into this place!

Study the drawing provided. Find 5 pairs of identical items that have become separated in this messy room. (Answers on page 233.)

MATCH IT #2

66

Ready for a slightly tougher assignment? Read on!

Using the same drawing, find 5 pairs of objects that, while not identical, belong together—such as a cup and saucer would, or even a horse and carriage. (Answers on page 233.)

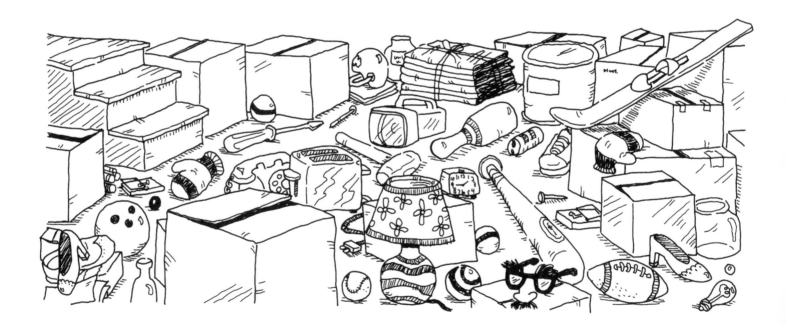

I SPY

There are so many different ways to play I Spy. Here is one of our favorites.

This game is a bit more challenging for the player who is the Spy. First, he or she looks for an object that everyone can see. Then, instead of giving a clue about the color or letters used to spell the object, the person who is the Spy gives only a general clue.

For example, if playing in a restaurant, the Spy might say, "I spy something that people listen to." What could this be? A jukebox? A telephone? A speaker? Other people? All players get 1 guess for each clue offered. When someone guesses the answer, that person takes over as the Spy.

TRAVEL TRIVIA
The lowest place in the United States is Death Valley, California. The area is 282 feet below sea level.

BILLBOARD RACE

67

Use billboards as building blocks to spell your chosen word.

Players each choose the name of an animal (or any other subject category). Names should have the same number of letters (such as "dog" and "cat" or "penguin" and "ostrich").

Each player searches passing billboards for the letters to spell out his or her chosen animal's name. Only the first letter of the words you see on billboards can be used. Also, letters must be found in the order that they appear in the word—no jumping ahead! When you see a billboard that has the word with the first letter you need, call it out. Then the other players can't use that billboard.

STOP SIGNS

Someone's been making faulty signs, and it's up to you to STOP it!

A heavy sign recently fell on our sign painter's head, and since then he has mixed up a few stop signs. Help him sort out his mistakes by finding the 3 pairs of signs that match. (Answers on page 233.)

I CLAIM IT

Use your own special cards to play this fast-moving game.

You Will Need: Game cards you made in Chapter 1 (see #18), a stopwatch or clock

Start the clock and quickly turn the first 5 cards up, laying them side by side where all the players can see them. For the next 5 minutes, everybody should be on the lookout to see if any of the items pictured can be seen in real life from the car. The first person to see something that matches one of the cards calls out "I claim it" and takes the card. For example, if one of the cards has a picture of a police car on it, then the first person to see a police car and say "I claim it" wins the card.

If all 5 cards are claimed before the time is up, lay out the next 5 cards and set the clock for another 5 minutes. If there are any cards left over, put them at the bottom of the deck. Once all of the cards have been claimed, see which player has collected the most.

ARTS & CRAFTS

All of the activities in this chapter involve making things—things to play with, things to wear, things you can hang up as art, practical things you can use on your trip, and even a few silly things that will make you laugh. Because some of the materials you'll need can be difficult to find while you're traveling, it's a good idea to read this chapter before you leave home. Make a list of the materials you want, and see how much of it you can find around the house. The rest can be purchased at hardware, grocery, or art supply stores.

SEWING CARDS

71

Who says you need needle and thread to sew? Use yarn to decorate these special shapes that you cut out.

You Will Need: Sturdy cardboard (measuring about 6×6 inches for each card), scissors, hole punch, yarn (about 2 feet for each card), clear tape

Make several outline drawings—animals, people, whatever you want—on a piece of cardboard, then ask mom or dad to help you cut out the shapes. Punch holes around the edges every ½ inch or so. Next, tie a knot in one end of a piece of yarn, then wrap a small piece of tape around the other end (just like on the end of a shoelace) so that you can easily push the yarn through the holes in the cardboard. After you're done, sew the card by threading the holes with different pieces of colored yarn.

You can even try sewing different pieces together to make 3-dimensional shapes. For example, sew 6 squares together to make a cube. Sew 8 triangles to make a diamond, or 4 triangles and 1 square to make a pyramid. What other shapes can you make?

WHIRLIGIG

These spectacular spinners make even a little breeze seem like a big deal!

You Will Need: 1 square piece of cardstock (at least 6×6 inches), scissors, pencil, ruler, ¼-inch wood dowel, thumbtack

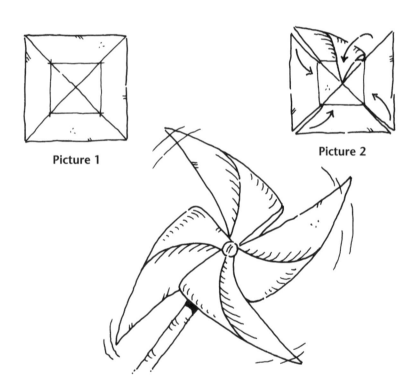

Picture 1

Picture 2

Draw 2 diagonal lines from the opposite corners of your cardstock (Picture 1). Starting at each corner, cut halfway down each line. Be careful not to cut any farther. Fold the corners down as shown (Picture 2). Hold the wood dowel behind the whirligig, and bend the left corner of each side of the square to meet in the center. Be sure not to crease the fold!

From the front, push the thumbtack through all 4 corners of the paper and into the wood. (Leave a little bit of the tack sticking out. If you push it all the way into the wood, the whirligig won't whirl.) Blow into the center of your whirligig, or hold it out while you run, and watch it spin!

TRAVEL TRIVIA
The crack in Philadelphia's famous Liberty Bell appeared in 1846, when it was rung in honor of George Washington's birthday.

CARDBOARD LOOM

73

With this simple loom, you can create cool, one-of-a-kind wall hangings to use as gifts or to hang in your room.

You Will Need: 1 piece of cardboard (8×12 inches; the bottom of a gift box is good), 2 smooth sticks (at least 10 inches long; dowel rods will work), various colored yarn, scissors

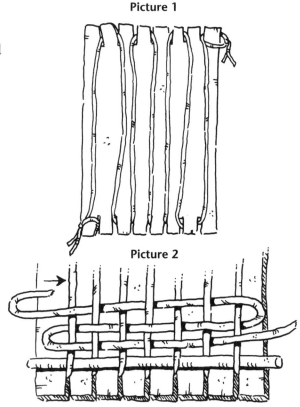

Picture 1

Picture 2

Ask a grown-up to help you make 7 cuts (about 1 inch apart and 1 inch deep) at the bottom and top of the cardboard (Picture 1). These flaps will hold your yarn as you weave. Thread your loom by tying a piece of yarn around the bottom left-hand corner. Carry the string up to the cut at the top left, around the back to the second cut, then back down the front to the bottom edge again.

Continue until the whole loom is strung, then tie the end of your yarn to the top right-hand corner, just as you did at the beginning. Weave a smooth stick or dowel rod through the bottom of the loom—over, under, over, under (Picture 2). Pull it snug against the bottom of the yarn loops, but don't pull it all the way off the loom yet. This stick will be the bottom frame of your wall hanging when you are finished.

Now it's time to start weaving your yarn back and forth across the loom, using whatever color you like. You can also weave pieces of ribbon, grasses, flowers, or even other sticks through the loom to create a one-of-a-kind pattern. As you weave, push the layers of yarn down against the bottom stick. This makes what is called a tight weave. Be careful: Don't pull the yarn too tight as you weave or you'll squeeze your wall hanging out of shape. When you get a few inches from the top, weave the other smooth stick through the top of the loom. This stick will be the top frame of your wall hanging.

Finish weaving, getting as close to the top stick as you can. Have a grown-up help you pull your wall hanging off the loom by carefully bending the cardboard flaps upward. Tie a piece of yarn to each end of the top stick so you can hang up your work of art.

MAKE A FAN

What can you do if your air conditioner breaks? Keep your cool by making your own fan!

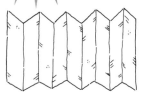

You Will Need: 1 sheet of notebook paper, tape, small loop of yarn (at least 8 inches long)

Fold the sheet of notebook paper back and forth in ½-inch sections from top to bottom as shown. Fasten one end of it closed with a piece of tape. Spread out the other end to make a fan. (HINT: Flatten the outer edges a little to help it stay open.)

If you want to make a fancy fan, draw a design along the top edge before you start folding. Another option is to tape a small loop of yarn to the bottom of the fan so you can carry it around your wrist.

CRAZY FACE

75

Save wear and tear on your own face by making this delightful crazy face do some of the work!

You Will Need: 1 white paper plate, at least 2 strips of white paper (1×11 inches), crayons, scissors

Make 4 slits in the top third of the paper plate and 2 slits in the bottom third of your plate, each about 1½ inches long. Thread 1 strip of paper through the top slit and bottom slits as shown. Don't pull them all the way through.

On the top strip of paper, draw a pair of eyes. When you finish that pair, move the strip of paper to the right until they disappear. Now draw a different pair of eyes. Make them mad, glad, goofy, or sleepy. The crazier the better! On the bottom strip of paper, draw different mouths, just as you did for the eyes. When you're finished, move the strips back and forth. How many wacky faces can you make? Make new strips, if you want, or make a new face with 3 rows of slits—one for eyes, one for mouths, and one in the middle for noses!

76 DRINKING STRAW LOOM

Drinking straw looms are simple and easy to make—and they can even help you hold up your pants!

You Will Need: Yarn (or jute, or string), 7 drinking straws

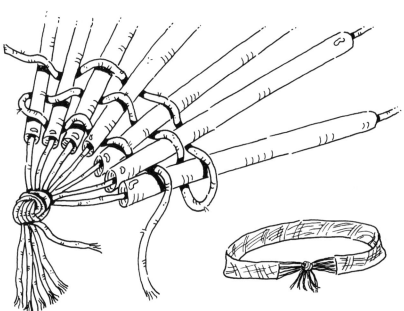

Ask a grown-up to help you measure around your waist where a belt would go. Add 8 inches to that number. Let's say your waist is 20 inches around. Adding 8 gives you 28 inches. Cut 7 pieces of yarn to that length.

Tie the pieces of yarn together at one end, leaving 4 inches free above the knot. Slip a drinking straw over each piece of yarn, pushing up against the knot. The straws will hold the yarn straight as you weave. Take another piece of yarn (the same or a different color), and tie one end of it to the same knot as the others. Weave this piece of yarn over and under each straw, then back again. After you make 2 rows, gently slip the drinking straws down a little. Push the rows together and pull the yarn tight as you go, or else you'll have a very loose belt. If you want to change colors of yarn, tie a new piece of yarn to the old piece and keep weaving.

Tie off the belt 4 inches from the end. Put it around your waist and tie the loose ends together. You've just completed your very own handmade belt!

TRAVEL TRIVIA
The five Great Lakes are the largest group of freshwater lakes in the world. If the water they contain were spread evenly across the entire United States, the depth would reach more than 6 feet.

FINGER PUPPETS

77

These are so easy and fun to make, you just might end up with more puppets than fingers!

You Will Need: Paper, markers or crayons, scissors, tape or glue stick

Cut out a piece of paper about 2×3 inches and fold as shown. Use tape or glue stick to fasten the paper where it folds over. Decorate the front so that your puppet looks like a person or animal.

Now you are ready to start the show! Make up a story to tell with your puppets, or have someone read out of a book while you act out the words. You can even give a little show for people in other cars as they pass by!

TOE PUPPETS

78

Foot theater can be even more entertaining than finger theater—after all, it has much more "sole!"

You Will Need: Paper, markers or crayons, scissors, tape or glue stick

Copy the pattern shown onto your paper, and cut it out as shown. Make 2 cuts where the dotted lines are. (NOTE: You may want to change where these cuts go if your toes are bigger or smaller.) Decorate the front so that your toe puppet looks like you want it to. Hook the 2 slits together so that you have a band to slip over your toe. Glue or tape if you need to.

DOLLAR BILL RING

You can make a unique finger ring out of a dollar bill—and you won't need scissors or glue!

You Will Need: A 1-dollar bill

Hold the dollar bill with Washington's face up. Fold in the thin white borders on the top and bottom of the bill (Picture 1). Now fold the top half down (Picture 2). Fold the bill in half again (Picture 3). Now turn the bill lengthwise and fold down the white border again (Picture 4). Fold down the top ¾ inch of the bill so you can see the word and number "one" (Picture 5).

Turn the bill over. Fold up the bottom so that it makes a flap (Picture 6). Now fold this flap down to the right (Picture 7). Turn the bill around, and hold it as shown (Picture 8). Wrap the part that's sticking up back and around your finger (Picture 9). Lift up the flap with the word "one" on it and fold over the other flap (Picture 10). Fold the "one" back down again, and tuck the white margin underneath (Picture 11). The remaining flap is folded under and tucked into the triangle pocket inside the ring (Picture 12).

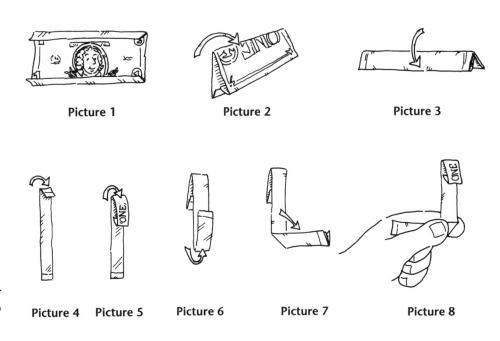

Picture 1   Picture 2   Picture 3

Picture 4   Picture 5   Picture 6   Picture 7   Picture 8

Picture 9   Picture 10   Picture 11   Picture 12

FRIENDSHIP BRACELETS

Friendship bracelets tell your friends and family how special they are—so make a bunch and give them all away!

You Will Need: Embroidery floss, scissors, tape (or someone to hold the end for you)

There are many bracelet patterns. This one is so easy it braids itself! Cut 6 pieces of embroidery floss, each 24 inches long. Pick whatever colors you like. Tie the strings together with a knot about 3 inches from the top. Tape the knotted end to a table or wall, or have a friend hold the end for you while you work.

Twist all the pieces together tightly, starting near the knot and moving down (Picture 1). Make a very tight twist about 14 inches long. Leave about 3 inches, and tie the ends together like you did to start. Now hold the end of the twist with one hand. Press down in the middle of the twist with the pointer finger of your other hand (Picture 2). Fold the twist in half, making sure both sides are even.

Take your pointer finger out of the middle, and watch the bracelet braid itself! It's okay if the twist gets bunched up. You can straighten it out. Remove the tape, or have your friend let go of the end. Tie the 2 ends together into a big knot. To wear your bracelet, pull the knot through the loop in the other end of the bracelet (Picture 3).

Picture 1

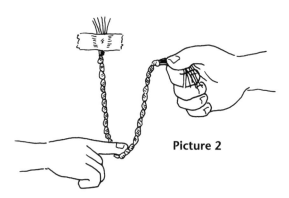

Picture 2

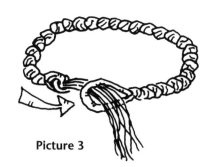

Picture 3

GOD'S EYE

81

The Pueblo and other Native Americans wore special decorations called god's eyes, which were thought to bring good luck and long life. Here's how to make your own.

You Will Need: 2 sticks the same size (cotton swabs, pencils, or ice-cream sticks will work), yarn (several colors look prettiest) or string

Place 2 sticks together to form an X. This is the frame for your god's eye. Tie one end of the yarn around the center of the crossed sticks to hold them together. Make the knot tight so the sticks aren't loose (Picture 1). Hold the frame in one hand and keep the sticks in place. With the other hand, wrap the yarn over and around one arm of the X, then over and around the next arm, and so on (Picture 2). Pull the yarn tight each time. Every time you wrap an arm, push the yarn down snugly toward the center. Continue working this way until the god's eye is completed (Picture 3).

You can wrap the entire X with the same color yarn, or you can add different colors. To start a new color, tie the end of the old color yarn to an arm of the X. Make a double knot. Now start a new color of yarn in the same place by tying it on. Continue wrapping. You can add as many colors as you like. Once you get the hang of making god's eyes, try making a gigantic one using 2 rulers, or a tiny one using toothpicks!

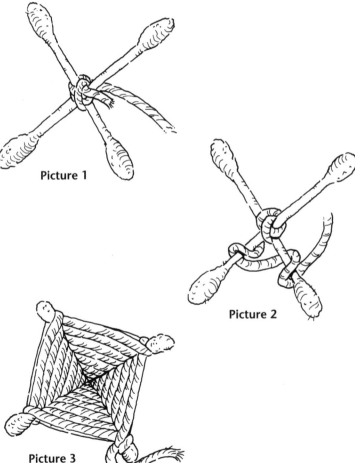

Picture 1

Picture 2

Picture 3

82

SQUEALERS

You can make a wild squealer with just about any small piece of paper!

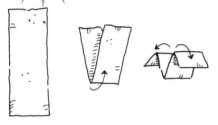

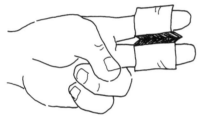

You Will Need: 1 small piece of paper (1×4 inches works well)

Fold the paper in half, then fold the ends down about ½ inch. Hold the paper between your 2 fingers as shown. Now press the paper against your lips. Spread the paper apart very slightly—just a crack, really. Now blow hard into the paper! If you don't hear a loud squealing sound, try spreading the paper less or more.

If you open and close the paper slightly as you blow, you can change the sound of your squealer. If you practice, you might even be able to play a song!

CRAYON RUBBINGS

83

Here's a different kind of "picture" to help you remember your trip.

You Will Need: Blank white paper, pencil or crayons, a couple of small objects (coins or keys will do)

Put a coin under a piece of paper. Peel a crayon so you can hold it flat against the paper and rub it gently across the coin. Hold the coin down with your thumb and pointer finger. Rub just hard enough to make the shapes on the coin stand out. Try not to let the coin slip as you rub. Don't rub too hard or else you'll get nothing but a blob. You'll soon see an interesting "snapshot" of what the object looks like.

Leaves are another good thing to practice on, but you can also make rubbings out of plaques, engravings on buildings, or even grave markers.

TRI-BOOMERANG

This cardboard boomerang will keep coming back for more!

You Will Need: 1 piece of heavy cardboard (5×5 inches) for each boomerang, pencil, scissors

Boomerangs started out as hunting weapons, but they're fun to play with as toys. This special 3-arm boomerang is great for the beach, rest stop, or park. Simply copy the boomerang design onto cardboard and cut it out. (You can make bigger ones later after you get the hang of throwing this one.)

There are 2 ways to throw your boomerang. One way is to grab the boomerang lightly by one leg, hold it up by your head so the flat part is facing your ear, then throw it up into the air in front of you. (Don't throw it straight.) Another way is to grab the boomerang lightly by one leg, hold it out at your side so the flat part is facing the ground, then throw it slightly up and in front of you with a quick flip of the wrist.

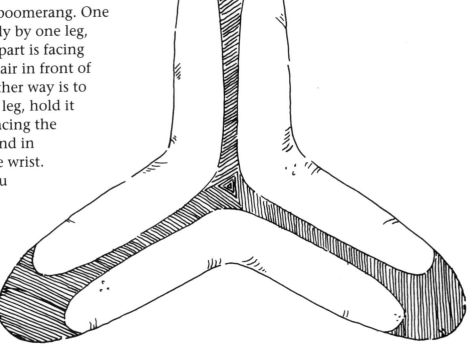

Depending on the cardboard you use and how you throw it, your boomerang might fly in a big curve and come right back to you. It might even fly completely around behind you! Change the way your boomerang flies by bending and twisting the arms very slightly. Experiment to see what works best.

POPPERS

Pop goes the paper with this popper you fold yourself.

You Will Need: 1 sheet of paper (8½×11 inches)

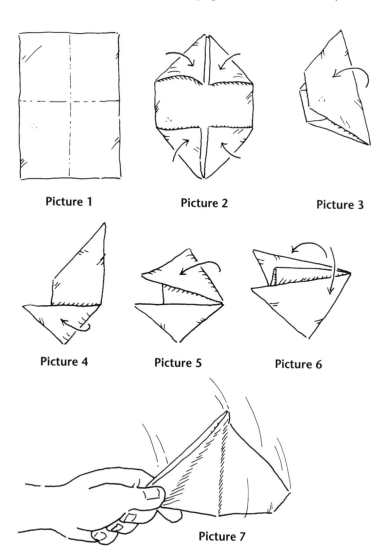

Picture 1

Picture 2

Picture 3

Picture 4

Picture 5

Picture 6

Picture 7

Fold the paper in half and then in half again. Now unfold it (Picture 1). Next, fold the corners down to the middle (Picture 2), then fold the paper in half (Picture 3). Now fold the bottom up to the middle (Picture 4) and the top down to the middle (Picture 5). Finally, fold the top of the paper down again, this time toward the back (Picture 6).

Hold the popper at the very tip (Picture 7). Give it a sharp downward snap, and it will open with a bang. If it doesn't, open the popper and bend all the creases back and forth several times to loosen them up. Then refold and try again. Notebook and other lightweight paper works best.

COOL STOOL

86

If you're tired of sitting on the ground when you go camping, try this easy-to-make 3-legged stool.

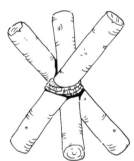

You Will Need: 3 straight sticks, each about the same size (1 foot long, 1 inch thick) and as smooth as possible, 2 feet of rope or heavy twine. If you have trouble finding 3 sticks the same size, have a grown-up help you cut a long stick into 3 equal pieces and smooth out any pointy parts.

Wrap the rope or twine several times around the sticks, and tie them together with a strong knot. To open up your 3-legged stool, twist the sticks out and away from each other as shown. Sit on your stool by positioning 1 stick between your legs and 2 sticks along your bottom. You'll be surprised at how comfortable your stool is—and no more wet pants from sitting on damp ground!

PRESSED PLANTS

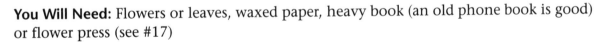

87

Use your flower press to save flowers and other plants you find.

You Will Need: Flowers or leaves, waxed paper, heavy book (an old phone book is good) or flower press (see #17)

Years ago, people used to dry flowers as a way of remembering summer in the middle of winter. You can dry flowers, too. A flower press works best, but if you haven't made one yet, you can use a heavy book.

Thin, flat flowers work best for pressing. Carefully trim the stem and most of the leaves, then lay the flower flat on a paper towel. Cover the flower with another layer of paper towel. Then sandwich the whole thing between 2 pieces of waxed paper. (The waxed paper keeps the damp flower from damaging the book as it dries.) Put your flower "sandwich" in the middle of a big book or in your flower press.

Let your flowers dry for a couple of weeks. (The petals should sound like paper when you touch them gently). Once they are dry, you can glue them to pieces of cardboard or paper to make wall hangings, book-marks, stationary, or book covers.

88 MACARONI JEWELRY

If you get bored in the back of the car, string your own necklaces, bracelets and anklets!

You Will Need: Any kind of pasta or macaroni with holes in it (elbow, wagon wheel, etc.), strong thread or dental floss, markers

Color the macaroni with markers if you want, making stripes, solids, dots, and checkers, then measure out about 30 inches of thread. Decide which piece if any will be in the center of the string. Start by stringing pieces of macaroni on either side of this piece. The pieces can be any shape or color, but try to keep them even on both sides.

When your necklace, bracelet, or anklet is long enough, tie a button onto one end of the thread. Tie a small loop in the other end. Slip the button through the loop to fasten it around your neck, wrist, or ankle.

PAPERCOPTERS 89

These paper helicopters spin just like the real thing!

Picture 1

Picture 2

Picture 3

Picture 4

You Will Need: Strips of heavy paper or cardboard (1×10 inches), small paper clips, markers or crayons

Fold a strip of paper in half (Picture 1). Fold the ends down about 2 inches. Don't fold them straight down. Instead, fold them at a slight angle (Picture 2). Next, push a paper clip onto the bottom, and fold the wings out (Picture 3). Hold your papercopter by the paper clip, and throw it into the air. Watch it spin (Picture 4). Decorate your papercopter with markers or crayons.

Experiment. What happens if you add more paper clips to the bottom? Or use a longer strip of paper to make your papercopter? Or fold the wings so they have more (or less) angle?

MATCH-UP BOOKS

Create your own collection of kooky characters.

You Will Need: 2 sheets of white paper (8½×11 inches), 1 piece of light cardboard, pencil or crayons, stapler, scissors

Cut each sheet of paper into 3 equal-sized rectangles. (Cut across the short side of the paper.) This gives you 6 rectangles. Cut a piece of light cardboard to be the same size. Stack the 6 paper rectangles on top of each other. Fold them down twice, dividing the papers into 3 sections.

Unfold the rectangles and draw a different person, family member, animal, or monster on each page. Draw the head in the top square, the body in the middle square, and the legs at the bottom. (NOTE: The drawings should all be about the same size, and the heads, bodies, and legs should all line up in the same place. This way the head of one person will line up with the body on every other drawing.)

After you finish drawing, put the piece of cardboard on the bottom of the stack. Then staple the left side of your drawings together to make a book. Carefully cut across the papers along the folds, stopping before you get to the staples. (Don't cut through the cardboard!) Your book is done. Flip through your book, turning different flaps at a time, to see what silly characters you can create!

TRAVEL TRIVIA

Wilbur and Orville Wright made the first manned airplane flight at Kitty Hawk, North Carolina, in 1903. The flight lasted only 12 seconds.

STRAW GLIDER

This may not look like any paper airplane you've ever seen—but it flies!

You Will Need: 1 strip of heavy paper (1½×8 inches), 1 strip of heavy paper (1×6 inches), drinking straw, tape

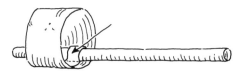

Picture 1

Roll each strip of paper into a circle, taping the large circle to one end of the straw as shown (Picture 1). Tape the small circle to the other end of the straw (Picture 2).

To fly your glider, hold the straw between the 2 hoops of paper and throw gently. You'll be surprised how well it flies!

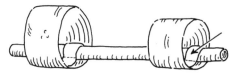

Picture 2

TRAVEL TRIVIA

The first permanent European settlement in North America was established at St. Augustine, Florida, in 1565.

ROCK MENAGERIE

92

A pet rock doesn't need any food, and it always stays where you tell it.

You Will Need: Collected rocks, paint or markers

Search a beach or forest trail for unusually shaped stones that are about the size of a Ping-Pong ball. As you look at each stone, turn it in different directions. Does the shape remind you of anything? Maybe it looks like a turtle, the head of a wolf, or a dinosaur, or a cat's paw. When you get home, wash the rocks with soap and water, then let them dry.

Using poster paints or markers, decorate your stones so they look like animals—with eyes, noses, and mouths. Make cages for your animals out of Popsicle sticks. You can even create a rock circus with lions, tigers, bears, elephants, and horses.

DANDELION ART

93

Did you know that dandelion means "lion's tooth" in French? In summertime, you can use the plants to make lovely chains and wreaths.

You Will Need: A handful of dandelions

To make a dandelion chain, pluck the flower so that you have as much of the stem as possible. Remove the flower part. Dandelion stems are hollow, so you can loop the stem into a circle and put the small end of the stem inside the large end of the stem. Repeat the first 2 steps with another flower stem, connecting the 2 links before you close the stem, as shown (Picture 1). How long can you make your dandelion chain?

Picture 1

To make a wreath, keep the flower parts on. First, tie a loose knot near the bottom of a dandelion stem, then slip the stem of another flower through the middle of the knot (Picture 2). Gently tighten the knot so that the stem won't come out. Now tie a knot in the end of the flower stem that you just added to your wreath. Keep adding flowers until your chain is as long as you want, then link them together into a wreath by tying the last stem to the first flower. If you like, you can make a small wreath to wear as a headpiece.

Picture 2

PHOTO CARDS

94

If you can't find a postcard that really catches your eye, make your own with the pictures you take.

You Will Need: Photographs, heavy paper, glue stick, scissors, pencil

Hold a photo against the paper with one hand, and with the other, carefully trace the outside edge of the photo with a pencil. Carefully cut out the outline you just made, and then use your glue stick to glue the paper to the back of your photograph. (Make extra sure that the edges are glued well, so they don't come apart in the mail.)

Draw a line down the middle of the back of postcard. Put your message on the left side of the line and the address on the right side of the line. Leave room for a stamp in the upper right-hand corner.

FLY CATCHER

Catch flies with this magical contraption, then make them disappear!

You Will Need: One 8×8-inch piece of paper, crayons or markers

Fold the piece of paper in half and then in half again. Now unfold it (Picture 1). Starting over again, fold all 4 corners down to the middle (Picture 2), then flip the paper over. Fold all 4 corners down to the middle again (Picture 3).

Draw tiny flies and other bugs on 2 of the flaps as shown (Picture 4). Now bring corners A, B, C, and D together. Put your fingers under the flaps beneath the fly catcher (Picture 5). By opening and closing the device in different directions, you can see how the flies seem to appear and disappear.

To perform the trick, pretend to grab something from the air, then show your friends the flies you caught (Picture 6). Before anyone has a chance to take a closer look, pretend to shake them out. By secretly opening the fly catcher the other way, you can show that the flies have vanished!

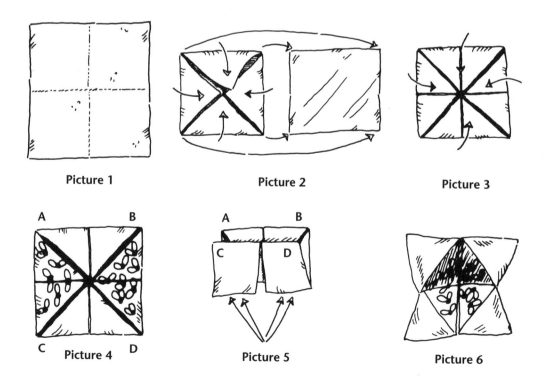

Picture 1 Picture 2 Picture 3

Picture 4 Picture 5 Picture 6

IMAGINATION GAMES

Design a castle. Make up a story. Imagine what it's like to be a bird. Except for a handful of drawing exercises, most of the activities in this chapter require no materials whatsoever. All that's needed is an open mind and a bit of imagination—something most youngsters have plenty of. Best of all, there are no wrong answers, and anything is possible. Imagination games allow us to indulge our fantasies and look at common things in new ways. Along the way, they provide an opportunity to learn something about ourselves and the world we live in.

BE A PSYCHIC

96

Test your hidden powers of communication. Can you send messages to someone without using pencil and paper, pantomimes, or your voice?

Have you ever wanted to let someone know what is on your mind without other people knowing it? Better yet, perhaps you've wanted to read someone else's thoughts. You can see for yourself how well you do by performing this simple exercise.

You and your partner need to sit so that you can look at each other's faces comfortably. Hold a magazine or book in front of you so that your partner can't see what you're looking at, then choose a word or picture to concentrate on. Look your partner in the eye, and repeat the word you've chosen to yourself—just be careful not to move your lips! See if you and your partner can communicate this way.

A large red beach ball.

It's red, round and bouncy.

BUILD A CASTLE

97

Think about what you would do if you could design your own dream castle.

What would your castle look like? Where would you build it? How many rooms would it have, and what would you put in each room? What kind of special rooms would you want for your hobbies? What sort of animals would you keep nearby? Who would live with you, and who would visit? What would you show people first? What else can you describe about your dream castle?

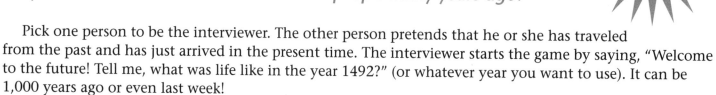

TRAVEL TRIVIA
More peanuts–and timber–are grown in Georgia than in any other state.

FREEZE FRAME

98

Do you ever wonder what life was like for people many years ago?

Pick one person to be the interviewer. The other person pretends that he or she has traveled from the past and has just arrived in the present time. The interviewer starts the game by saying, "Welcome to the future! Tell me, what was life like in the year 1492?" (or whatever year you want to use). It can be 1,000 years ago or even last week!

Then the other person can describe to the interviewer what it was like. Players from the past can ask questions of their own, such as "What would you like to know about life in 1492?" or even "What is life like for you in the 1990s?" Remember, there are no wrong answers! Just let your imagination carry you away.

GIRAFFELOPES

Create your own zoo of unusual animals by playing this truly wild game!

Use your imagination to create a zoo full of animals that nobody has ever seen before. Imagine the possibilities if you could mix and match any animal—for example, combining giraffes and antelopes to make giraffelopes.

To find your own animal combinations, you and another person each think of one real animal and then call out your choices at the same time. Then, name your new creation by combining the original names.

Now imagine you have some visitors looking at your new creation—of course, they've never seen it before—and it is up to you to tell them about it. Describe as much as you can about the new animal you've created. What does it look like? How much does it weigh? How does it move? What does it eat? Where does it live? What else can you say about your creation?

MOTORCYCLE PURSUIT

When there's nothing to do but stare out the window, you can get mighty tired of watching the same stuff go by. But here's an imagination game that will make time fly.

Imagine that someone is riding next to your car on a motorcycle. But he's not riding on the road. He's riding on the hills and valleys and bumps and ditches beside the road! He can jump over street signs, bushes, and anything else that gets in his way, but sometimes he takes a tumble. Now imagine him jumping back on the motorcycle and catching up to your car. He's going fast! Follow his path for him and imagine how many tricks he can do.

BIG AS CAN BE

101

More people work in Chicago's Sears Tower and New York's World Trade Center every day than live in some towns. Think about it!

Imagine that you are as tall as the tallest building you have ever seen. What does the world look like to you? Can you talk to birds, planes, and blimps? Can you feel the elevators going up and down inside you? Can you hear the people talking in your rooms and hallways?

Now imagine that you are as big as a mountain. Your head is always in the clouds, and you wear a thick patch of snow for a cap year-round. A million trees grow on your skin. You are too big and steep to build a road over, so someone built a tunnel through you that is 2 miles long. Thousands of cars drive through the tunnel everyday. Do they tickle your mountain feet? Can you feel the hikers camping on your skin? Do you have any mountain neighbors? Are you found in the jungles of South America, the forests of New England, or the icy glaciers of Canada?

CAVE SURPRISE

102

What would you do if it happened to you?

You've decided to take a summer hike, so you're walking down a path in a friendly forest. You hear birds singing and the rustling sound of leaves beneath your feet. You watch the squirrels and chipmunks chase one another from the path as they hear you approach. Up ahead you see the path divide in 2 directions. To your right, the path leads to a beach with sunbathers and rowboats. To your left, the path leads to the opening of a cave that looks just a little bit taller than you. You decide to check out the cave, which looks dark and quiet on the outside. But after you take a few steps inside, you hear a low growl.

What happens next? Finish the story in your own words. See how many different endings you can create. Be sure to give each story a separate title.

VOLCANO ALERT

What would you do if it happened to you?

You're a famous scientist who has been working for years on a small, remote island in the South Pacific, where you have found dozens of rare plants and animals that the world has never seen. You are very close to making an important discovery that may change the way the rest of the world thinks! Few people live here because for the past 400 years the island's volcano has been very active. Since you arrived the volcano has been strangely silent. But lately the local people have started talking about the "thunder without light."

Another team of scientists has just arrived by plane to help you finish up your work. You are giving them a tour of the island when suddenly the ground starts to shake and you hear a loud booming noise. People are yelling in the distance. You look up at the sky, which is thick with smoke.

What happens next? Finish the story in your own words. See how many different endings you can create.

CAR CHARADES

Here is a great guessing game for 2 or more people traveling by car.

Have you ever been talking to someone when all of a sudden you can't think of a word you want to say? One solution is to act out what you're trying to communicate. Car Charades is a game in which you try to say something using only your hands and face. Before you begin, each player spends a few quiet minutes looking outside at the scenery for some ideas of what he or she will act out for the other players. It is best to write down what you are trying to act out. Take turns trying to guess what each person is trying to say.

THE KLUM-KLUM BIRD

105

What would you do if it happened to you?

You work as a wilderness guide, helping visitors find their way through the thick layers of trees and rivers of the forest. You've been hired by Livingston Stanley, a famous museum owner searching for a feather from the tail of the Klum-Klum bird.

It has rained and thundered for 3 days and nights as you paddle the crookedest river in the forest. The water is high and the rapids are dangerous. As the rain drips into your eyes, you see a bright flash of light! A towering tree just ahead has been hit by lightning. It crashes into the river, blocking your way. You try to turn your canoe to shore before you crash into the tree.

What happens next? Finish the story in your own words. See how many different endings you can create.

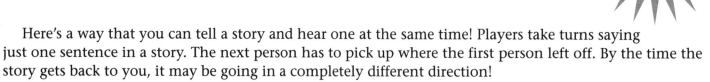

TRAVEL TRIVIA
The place where sunlight first touches the United States each morning is at the top of Cadillac Mountain in Maine's Acadia National Park.

TAG-TEAM STORY

106

The best stories are built one sentence at a time.

Here's a way that you can tell a story and hear one at the same time! Players take turns saying just one sentence in a story. The next person has to pick up where the first person left off. By the time the story gets back to you, it may be going in a completely different direction!

HIDDEN MOUNTAIN VILLAGE

What would you do if it happened to you?

You're a mapmaker. For the past 3 days you have been traveling alone to measure a snowcapped mountain peak for your next map. The higher you climb, the thinner and colder the air becomes. All of a sudden, the wind begins to blow with the force of a giant. You decide to head back down the mountain, but just as you turn around, the snow flies into your face. You wander for what seems like days, seeing nothing but white, and finally stumble upon a small empty cabin. Entering it, you roll out your sleeping bag and quickly fall asleep.

When you wake up, the storm has ended. All is quiet. Feeling rested, you walk out of your cabin, which you discover has been sitting in the middle of a small village that doesn't appear on your map. Stranger still, there is no snow—it seems like spring. Dozens of people stop what they are doing when you walk out of the door. They're talking in a language you don't understand, wearing clothes you've never seen.

What happens next? Finish the story in your own words. See how many different endings you can create.

DRAWING CALMNESS

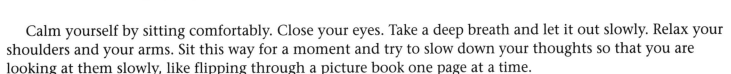

Most people can draw "things," but it's harder to draw feelings.

You Will Need: Paper, crayons or markers

Calm yourself by sitting comfortably. Close your eyes. Take a deep breath and let it out slowly. Relax your shoulders and your arms. Sit this way for a moment and try to slow down your thoughts so that you are looking at them slowly, like flipping through a picture book one page at a time.

What does calmness look like? What shape? What color? Is it light or dark? Soft or hard? Is it one big shape, or lots of small ones? Draw a picture of calmness.

DISTANT PLANET

What would you do if it happened to you?

The starship you are piloting has just made an emergency landing on the planet Karg. Luckily, none of your crew was hurt. After the computer makes sure the air outside is safe to breathe, you decide to do some exploring on this new planet. As soon as you pop the hatch, you can feel the heat of 3 suns in the sky. When you climb out onto the starship, you see a jungle in all directions. But it's the strangest jungle you've ever seen. Vines grow everywhere, like gigantic spiderwebs. And the trees! They all have 2 trunks and orange leaves. You can hear animals in the jungle making noises, but they're too shy to come close. Who knows what they look like!

Suddenly, you hear a buzzing noise behind you. It sounds like a giant bumblebee. As you glance over your shoulder, you see something that looks like a small hot-air balloon with wings. It lands next to your ship. A door in the side "wooshes" open and...

What happens next? Finish the story in your own words. See how many different endings you can create.

TRAVEL TRIVIA
Rhode Island, our smallest state, was the last colony to become a state. Delaware, our second-smallest state, was the first.

PIRATE ATTACK

What would you do if it happened to you?

You own a large sailboat and are sailing it around the world. Every day seems to bring a new adventure. Last week, you braved a 3-day storm. The week before, a giant whale surfaced next to your boat and blew a column of water 100 feet into the air. Today seems like a normal day. The clouds move quickly across the sky, and the ocean swells gently. You close your eyes to take a short nap.

Later, you're awakened by the sound of someone shouting in the distance. Who could it be, here in the middle of the ocean? Grabbing your telescope, you peer out and see an old-fashioned sailing ship with 5 masts and dozens of sails. The ship is flying a strange flag. As you look closer, you see a skull and crossbones. Pirates!

What happens next? Finish the story in your own words. See how many different endings you can create.

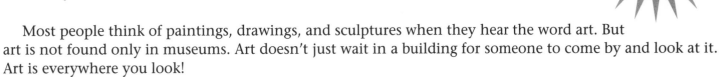

TRAVEL TRIVIA
Alaska's Mount McKinley is North America's highest mountain. It is 20,320 feet high.

WHO IS AN ARTIST?

You may be an artist and not even know it!

Most people think of paintings, drawings, and sculptures when they hear the word art. But art is not found only in museums. Art doesn't just wait in a building for someone to come by and look at it. Art is everywhere you look!

Did you know that musicians are artists, too? So are actors and writers. So are magicians and jugglers. Whenever you do something creative—dancing, singing, cooking, drawing—you're being an artist. How many different kinds of artists can you name? Are you an artist?

PENCIL OR MAGIC WAND?

112

How many different uses can you find for common, everyday objects?

Everybody knows that bricks are used to make buildings. But you can also use a brick as a paperweight or a doorstop. Or, you could use it as an anchor to keep a vulture from flying away. You might even use it to replace a giant's tooth!

Here is a list of some common items to get you started. For example, a spoon is for eating soup, but it could also be a tiny shovel, a catapult, or a lounge chair for a mouse.

Toothpick	Suspenders	Bathtub
Garden hose	Saltshaker	Car tire
Suitcase	Pillowcase	Harmonica
Broom	Baseball bat	Ice cube tray

DRAWING HAPPINESS

113

Different things make people happy, but the feeling is the same for everyone. Can you draw happiness?

You Will Need: Paper, crayons or markers

What makes you feel happy? A special person, place, or thing? Think about how you felt the last time you were very happy. What happened? How did you feel inside? Warm or bubbly or tingly or out of breath? What color is happiness? What shape? Try to draw it.

114

JUST IMAGINE

What would you do if...

...you grew wings overnight?
...you could see in the dark?
...you had 4 arms instead of 2?
...you could breathe underwater?
...you were 6 inches tall?
...your bones were made of rubber?
...you could play basketball better than Michael Jordan?
...you could talk to the trees in a forest?
...you had antennas instead of ears?
...you were a famous rock star?
...you could speak 20 languages?
...you became principal of your school?

TAG-TEAM ART

115

An artist can see a sunset in a line, a face in a circle, or a mountain in a squiggle on a page. What do you see?

You Will Need: Paper, pen or pencil

Art is twice as fun when you share the pencil! The rules are simple. Player 1 draws a line, squiggle or simple shape, on a piece of paper. As soon as you lift your pencil, it's the next player's turn. Player 2 takes the paper and adds another line, squiggle or shape, trying to turn the art into a picture.

Don't tell the other person what you are trying to draw. That might spoil some of the surprise. What you think is going to be a seagull might turn out to be a sunflower! See how long you can keep adding lines to your artwork. When you decide that your masterpiece is finished, start a new picture.

RADIO DRAWING

Turn music into art without opening your mouth!

You Will Need: Paper, crayons or markers

If you listen carefully, music that doesn't have any words can paint a picture in your mind. Turn on the radio and find a station that is playing music without words. Jazz or classical music works well.

Now close your eyes. How many different instruments can you hear? Do they sound like they're working with each other or against each other? Is one instrument easier to hear than the others? Is the music loud or soft? Does the music sound rushed and crowded, as if everything is hurrying to get to the next note? Or is it slow and lazy, as if the notes were taking a walk along the beach at sunset? What about the mood of the music? Does it sound happy? Sad? Sleepy? Excited?

What colors match the music that you're hearing? If the sounds were shapes on a page, what would they look like? Draw what you think the music would look like.

DRAWING SADNESS

It's easy to draw a sad face, but can you draw sadness a different way?

You Will Need: Paper, crayons or markers

Pretend that you've just met an alien who lives on another planet. On his planet, no one is ever sad. He asks you to draw a picture of sadness for him.

What would you draw? Think of a time when you or one of your friends was sad. What color do you feel inside? What shape do you feel in your heart? What kind of lines do you see in your head? Draw a picture of sadness.

NAME POEMS

You can make a poem appear out of anybody's name, just like a magician pulling a rabbit out of a hat!

You Will Need: Paper, pen or pencil

Anybody can write a poem about another person or a character in a book. First, write the name down the left-hand side of your paper. Then think of words that begin with each of those letters, but make sure they describe this person or character.

Once you've thought of all the words you need, read the name poem aloud and see if you have really captured his or her personality. Here's one based on a character named Peter from *The Tale of Peter Rabbit*, a popular old story by Beatrix Potter.

Proud
Entertaining
Tough
Eager
Rabbit

UP IN THE CLOUDS

118

119

If there are clouds in the sky, you've got endless possibilities for fun and games.

Look at the clouds above you, and trace with your finger the different shapes they take. Sometimes you can see what looks like faces, animals, or other familiar objects. If you can, pick a group of things (such as a collection of cartoon characters or various items from a favorite book you've read), and see how many things you can find from that group. Or, try naming something you see and then letting other people try to find it. If you watch the shapes long enough, you'll see them change as the clouds move.

SUPERHERO

120

Have you ever thought about living a life of high adventure? Going on daring rescue missions? Staying one step ahead of the bad guys?

Imagine that you are the hero of your own story. What would your name be? Would you have any secret powers or tools? How would you travel from place to place? Would you have a secret identity, or would everyone know who you are? Would you have a secret hiding place, like a bat cave? Who would you help? Would you do good deeds or try to solve crimes?

What else would you enjoy about being a superhero?

WRITE A HAIKU

121

Do you have a soft spot for short poetry? Then haiku is for you!

You Will Need: Paper, pen or pencil

Have you ever noticed how words seem to have beats to them? Hold your hand just below your chin and start reading this page slowly. Do you see how your chin rhythmically touches your hand while you speak? These beats are called syllables, and if you can count them, you can be a haiku poet.

Haiku poems have a very specific pattern. They have 3 lines and 17 syllables. The first and last lines have 5 syllables each, with 7 in the middle line. They are often written about animals and nature. Look around you and see what you can find to write about! Here are a few samples:

Looking at the green
Suddenly red, orange, and brown
Autumn is now here.

Roses growing in
A beautiful patch of red
Tugging at the fence.

A proud, silent crow
Sitting on top of the barn
Look at his feathers!

THE GAME GAME

If you find other board games boring, make your own with these simple directions!

You Will Need: Paper, pen or pencil

When you draw your own board game, you get to make up all the rules. And the coolest thing about it is you can make one anywhere—all you need is a sheet of paper and a pencil.

To get you thinking, we've given you 2 patterns and some directions that you might want to put on the different squares. You can make the game path like a winding sidewalk, like a coil that spirals around as you move, or some other shape. You can also put in "shortcuts" so that if a player lands on a certain square, he or she can cut over to a different part of the game.

Try putting some silly directions in the boxes, too, like "Howl like a wolf" or "Put your thumbs in your ears." And whenever you get bored with your board game, remember: You can always make another!

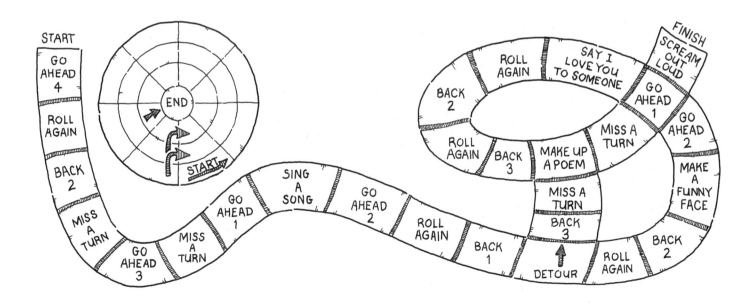

RIDDLEMAKER

It's easy to make your own riddles—if you just know a few easy tricks of the riddler's trade.

Think of something you want to make a riddle about. We'll do pigs as an example, because pigs are pretty funny creatures. Make a list of all the words you can think of that have to do with pigs. You might think of mud, hog, pork, bacon, and ham. Next, think of a pun you can make by rhyming one of those words with some other word. For example, "hog" rhymes with "dog."

Now put on your riddler's cap and think of a well-known saying, song, or phrase that has the word "dog" in it. For example, "It's raining cats and dogs." By switching the word "dog" for the word "hog," we have the answer to our riddle: "It's raining cats and hogs." Now we have to think of the riddle itself. How about this: What does a pig say during a thunderstorm? That's right: "It's raining cats and hogs!"

Here's another pig riddle using the word "pork": What is a pig's favorite town? Give up? New Pork City! See how many riddles you can make up.

SEEING IS BELIEVING

If you are tired of seeing the same things around you, follow these hints to change what you see!

If you need a change of pace in the things around you, challenge yourself to find it. First, think about where you'd rather be (perhaps on the ocean or in a desert), then look around to see what you would need to replace. Perhaps you can begin with the road becoming water or sand. Next you can watch the other cars around you become sailboats or camels that you're racing with. What else needs to change? See how many things you can transform.

NAME ART

Turn your name into a work of art!

You Will Need: Paper, pencil or crayons

Print your first name in large, neat letters. Now take a long look at them. What does the shape of each letter remind you of? A small letter "b" might be a baseball with a bat standing next to it. A capital "S" might be a snake or a pair of monkey arms. Try turning each letter into an object or animal so that your name looks like the things that interest you.

Can you do the same thing with your last name? What about other people's names?

REAL LIVE VIDEO

Have you ever thought about inventing your own video game?

If you could invent your own video game and play inside it, what kind of game would it be? What kind of character would you be? What special powers would you have? How would you keep score? How many levels would there be? What kind of opponents would you find? Where would all the secrets be hidden? How much would it cost to play your video game? Would you play it in the arcade, on a computer, or on a game deck? Would your friends and family be in the game? Who would they be?

FUTURE SHOCKED

What will the world be like in the far distant future?

Once you've played Freeze Frame (#98), you might want to try switching gears and playing Future Shocked. The basic idea is the same, but the interviewer in this game is talking to someone who came from 1,000 years in the future through a time machine. Here are some questions the interviewer can ask. What other questions can you ask the traveler from the future?

What is the name of the country you came from?
What is your job there?
What do you do for fun?
How do you travel?
What has happened between then and now?
How do people communicate?
What kind of food do you eat?
What sports do you play?

DRAWING FRIENDSHIP

Try to show what your feelings look like by drawing them.

You Will Need: Paper, crayons or markers

Think about your friends. Do you have different types of friends—maybe some from school, some from your church or synagogue, some from your neighborhood? What do you do together? How do you feel when you are together and when you're apart? How are your friends alike? How are they different?

What might friendship look like? Try to draw a picture of it.

DREAM VACATION

129

*If you could visit anywhere in the world—
or even outer space—where would you go?*

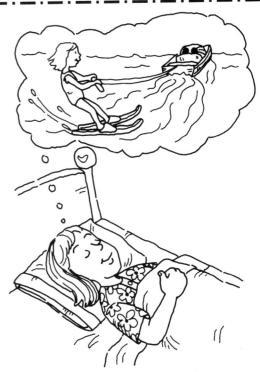

Is there someplace you've always wanted to visit? It doesn't have to be on this planet. It doesn't even have to be a real place! Think about your special dream vacation.

What is the name of the place you want to visit?
What will the weather be like there?
What are the people, plants, and animals like there?
How will you get there, and how long will it take?
What will you see first when you arrive?
Who will you visit first?
What will you do during the day? At night?
What will you take with you from home?
What will you bring back from your trip?

I LOVE A PARADE

130

*When was the last time you saw a parade? Now is the time to see the
one you've always wanted to see!*

You know that parades don't happen every day. Did you ever wonder why? Think about all the people you see marching by and all the planning needed to get them there. It takes a lot of work to make a parade happen. But you can see a parade every day if you take the time to create one in your mind.

Imagine yourself in charge of your very own parade. Here are some things you'll need to think about: What's the special occasion? Is this a parade for a holiday, or in honor of some hero? Who will be in the parade? Will you have clowns and jugglers? What kind of tricks will they perform? What kind of floats would you see? Will you invite marching bands? What music would they play?

FASTER THAN LIGHT

Did you know that light travels 186,000 miles every second? Compare that to a car, which might go 55 miles every hour.

Imagine you could run as fast as light. You could win a race with a jet plane. You could make it to the sun and back in about 7 hours! You could have a race with a sunbeam to see who could reach the earth faster.

In fact, you could run so fast that nobody would ever see you. Where would you go? What would you do? How would you stop? Would you need special shoes?

TEENY TINY

Try to imagine being smaller than small.

Can you hide under a grain of sand in the middle of a desert? Can you ride on a speck of dust floating by your window? Can you dangle your legs off the edge of a dime? Is your swimming pool a teaspoon of water?

What toys would you play with? A baseball would be bigger than a house. A doll would be bigger than a dinosaur. A crayon would be tall as a tree. A flashlight would be bigger than a lighthouse. A flea would be as big as a dog.

What would you eat? How would you talk to your friends? How could you write a letter or type on the computer? Maybe you're so small that you can only be seen with a microscope!

TALKING HANDS

When you can't use your voice, let your hands speak for you.

Because a large crowd can get mighty loud, umpires, referees, coaches, and players in sports use hand signals to talk to each other. Can you invent your own hand signals to mean certain things? For example, you could have a signal that means "Time for dinner!" or "What time is it?" or "Meet me on the corner!" or "Can I borrow a quarter?"

DRAWING SCARED

Use your imagination to draw how you feel when you're scared.

You Will Need: Paper, crayons or markers

Think about a time when you've been scared—but scared in a fun way, like when you're walking through a haunted house at Halloween, or listening to a ghost story around the campfire, or watching a monster movie. What does scariness look like? Is it dark and dreary like a cemetery at midnight, or is it bright and orange like a jack-o'-lantern? Draw a picture of it. See if you can do it with colors and shapes—without making a picture of something real.

TOOTHMOWERS

Did you ever wonder how some inventions get made?

On the count of 3, each player calls out the name of an object—animal, plant, tool, or other useful objects. For example, "tooth" and "lawnmower."

Now combine the words into one name, such as "toothmower." Describe what such an invention would look like. How would it work? What would you use if for? Where would you buy one? How much would it cost? And what would you do if your dentist pulled out a toothmower the next time you went to have your teeth cleaned?

AIRBORNE

Have you ever watched birds flying high above you and wondered what the world looked like through their eyes?

Think of a bird: A pigeon on a city sidewalk, a hawk soaring over a mountain, a duck in the marshy water, a penguin on an iceberg, or an owl roosting in a quiet country barn. Close your eyes and imagine being your favorite bird.

Where do you live? How far can you fly? What does the wind feel like beneath your wings? What kind of food do you eat? Where do you sleep? Do you like to fly at night or during the day? Do you live in the city or the country? How big are your wings? Do you fly south for the winter, or do you stay around when the snow comes? Do you like to swim?

TRAVEL TRIVIA
The state with the most lakes is Florida. The Sunshine State has more than 30,000.

SLOWER THAN MOLASSES

137

How slow can you go? As slow as a sloth waking up from a nap? As slow as honey dripping down a jar?

Imagine that you went about your ordinary day as slowly as a feather drifting from the sky. How long would it take for you to get to school? Try writing your name as slowly as you can, or brushing your teeth, or walking up the stairs, or singing your favorite song.

Have "slow races." Challenge a friend or family member to race across a room—but the last person to cross the finish line wins! The only rule: You must always keep moving. No fair just standing still!

BREAK-TIME GAMES

For most travelers, taking a break means pulling over at a roadside rest area, stopping at a restaurant for a meal, or ending the day at a nice hotel or motel. Each presents a different opportunity for fun and games—and a different challenge, too. Rest stops are perfect for noisier, more physically demanding games, while restaurants are ideal for quieter, low-impact activities that require no special materials and can be ended quickly when meals arrive. In hotels, the possibilities are more varied, ranging from board games and scavenger hunts to storytelling in the dark.

At the Rest Stop

138 ZEBRA

Clean out the car and have fun doing it with this simple basketball game.

You Will Need: A car full of trash (this should be easy to find during a long trip!), rest stop or parking lot with trash can

The object of the game is to toss all your trash into the trash can without missing. Every time you miss a shot, you get 1 letter in the word ZEBRA. If you miss 5 times, you spell the entire word and are out of the game.

You can add a twist to the game by including the following rule: If the other player makes a basket, you have to make your shot by standing in exactly the same place. If you miss, you get a letter; if you make it, you go again. Then if you make your next shot, the other player has to shoot from where you were standing. The last person left in the game is the winner.

DISK GOLF

Who needs clubs or balls—or holes—to play a round of golf?

You Will Need: A flying disk

The object of this game is to hit a series of targets in the fewest amount of throws. Start by planning your golf course. Look around you and choose 5 targets that you can safely hit with a disk without damaging them: big trees, fence posts, light poles, garbage cans, and so on. (A rest stop with lots of trees is a great place to play.) Make sure your targets aren't near parked cars or traffic. The targets should be at least 15 feet away, but if you're a better disk player, you can make them even farther apart.

Decide the throwing order for the targets. Each player takes turns trying to hit the targets. If you miss the target, you have to try again from the place where the disk lands. Keep going until you hit it. As soon as everyone has hit the target, players move on to the next one. Keep score by counting how many throws each player makes. At the end of your course, the player with the lowest score wins.

TRAVEL TRIVIA
The largest manmade hole in the United States is an open-pit iron ore mine at Hibbing, Minnesota. The largest working gold mine is in Lead, South Dakota.

VOLLEYBALL

You don't need a net or a ball to play this version of volleyball.

You Will Need: A ball or something that will work as a substitute (such as a rubber balloon filled with air, or wadded up newspaper)

This game is great for a rest stop because you can play a quick game in less than 10 minutes. First, find a "net"—a low fence, a picnic table, or even an open car door (just be sure you're well away from traffic). Take turns hitting the ball over the net. You can keep score if you want, but it's even more fun to see how long you can keep the ball in the air!

BODY BALL

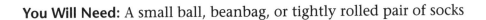

Stand in a circle, and see how long you can keep this ball in the air!

You Will Need: A small ball, beanbag, or tightly rolled pair of socks

Players try to keep the ball in the air as long as possible by hitting it with their feet, knees, head, shoulders, back of hand, arm, and so on. The only thing you can't use is the palm of the hand. How long can you keep the ball going?

GLUE TAG

You might get "stuck" playing this game.

This game is kind of like regular tag, except that tagged players must put their hands on the spot where they were tagged. If you're tagged 3 times, you're "it." A clever player will tag in awkward places, such as the lower leg or back. It's funny to watch players try to run with their hands "glued" to their legs!

CUP CATCH

A quick eye and a quick wrist will help you play this simple game of catch!

You Will Need: 2 empty cups, a ball or wadded up piece of paper

Players stand 5 feet apart. Using his or her cup, Player 1 throws the ball to Player 2, who must catch the ball in a cup. After every successful catch, both players take 1 step back. How far apart can you go and still catch the ball?

You can also play Cup Catch with 3 or more players. One variation is to eliminate players who drop the ball until only a single person—the winner—is left. To be fair, throw the ball high so players have time to get underneath it.

TRAVEL TRIVIA

New Hampshire has the shortest ocean coastline of any state—only 13 miles. Alaska has the longest ocean coastline—5,580 miles.

IRON & WOOD TAG

144

This game works a lot like regular tag, but with a twist.

In this game, you are safe from getting tagged only if you are touching something that is made out of wood. But be careful! If the player who is "it" shouts the word "iron," then you have to race to touch something metal because wood is no longer safe. Later, the player who is "it" can call out "wood" and make people scramble to find a tree, picnic table, and so on.

Two other special rules apply. Cars and other vehicles never count as metal objects, so you can't use them to be safe. Also, the player who is "it" must be at least 10 feet from the other players before calling out "iron" or "wood." It's not fair to stand right next to someone and then call it out!

145

MUSICAL PICNIC TABLE

Try this outdoor version of Musical Chairs.

You Will Need: Radio, picnic table or other large table, napkins (or cups or paper plates)

Before you begin, count how many people are playing. Then put that many napkins around the edge of the table, minus 1. So if you have 5 people playing, you will put 4 napkins around the table.

Have someone who is not playing put some music on the radio. Players walk around the table with their arms clasped behind their backs while the music plays. As soon as the music stops, players try to grab one of the napkins. The player who doesn't grab fast enough is out. Now reset the table, using 1 less napkin again, and repeat the process. The last person to grab a napkin wins.

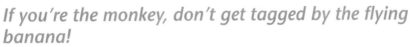

TRAVEL TRIVIA

The highest paved road in the United States is Colorado's Mount Evans Highway. The scenic roadway rises to a height of 14,264 feet.

MONKEY IN THE MIDDLE

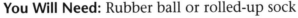

146

If you're the monkey, don't get tagged by the flying banana!

You Will Need: Rubber ball or rolled-up sock

Find an open place to play where you can make 2 bases about 20 feet apart (2 trees work really well). To play, 2 catchers stand near each base and throw the ball (the "banana") back and forth between them. The third player gets to be the monkey who runs back and forth between the bases and tries not to get tagged.

The catchers can tag the monkey only if they are holding the ball and touching the base with 1 foot at the same time. No fair throwing the ball at the monkey. If you tag the monkey, you get to switch places.

ELEPHANT WALK

Have you ever wondered what it would be like to be a wild animal?

Animals all have different ways of walking. Make a fun game by pretending to walk like your favorite animal. If you want, you can make some rules for the game. For example, you must change animals every time you touch something. If more than 1 person is playing, try to guess what animals everyone is pretending to be. You can even add noises if you like.

TRAVEL TRIVIA

California can boast the tallest trees in the world (redwoods) and the largest living things in the world (sequoia trees).

6-LEGGED RACE

Imagine how fast you would be if you had 6 legs instead of 2.

You Will Need: 2 towels or handkerchiefs, room to run

Players 1, 2, and 3 stand about 25 feet apart, either in a straight line or spread out in a triangle. Pick someone who's not playing to be the timekeeper. On "Go," Player 1 runs to Player 2. They tie their legs together just above the knee using the towel or handkerchief that Player 2 is holding. Together they run to Player 3, who is also holding a towel. Players 2 and 3 tie their legs together in the same way. Now all 3 players work together to run back to where Player 1 was standing at the start of the game.

How fast did you run on 6 legs? Can you improve your time if you do it again? What happens if you trade places? If you can find 3 more players, you can race each other as teams.

 **149**

RACES FOR ONE

Can you beat your PR?

You Will Need: A watch or stopwatch

PR stands for Personal Record. It's a way of saying what your best effort has accomplished. If the fastest time you've run across the playground is 15 seconds, for example, that's your PR for the playground. You can set PRs in just about any kind of race. Here are some ideas.

Pick a starting line and a finish line. Run from start to finish as fast as you can, and have someone time your speed. That's your PR for this course. Can you beat your PR in a second race?

Now try running the same race in different ways: skip; hop on both feet; hold one leg behind you by the ankle and hop on the other; crab walk (walk on your hands and feet at the same time, with the front side of your body pointing to the sky); or somersault (best done on soft grass). Write down your PR in every category, and see how the numbers compare with each other.

TRAVEL TRIVIA

Think of Kansas, and you think of wheat. During its early history, the nation's leading wheat producer was home to many Western legends, including Bat Masterson, Wyatt Earp, "Wild Bill" Hickok, and "Buffalo Bill" Cody.

RED LIGHT

The object of this game is to be the first player to reach the stoplight.

To play, pick someone to be the stoplight. The rest of the players stand shoulder to shoulder about 25 feet from the stoplight. The stoplight turns his or her back on the players and says, "Green light!" The players then run forward as fast as they can, trying to tag the stoplight.

The stoplight can turn around and yell, "Red light!" at any time. If you are caught moving when you should have stopped, you have to go all the way back to the starting line. So be ready to stop as quickly as you can, and don't move a muscle! The first person to tag the stoplight gets to be the stoplight next round.

CARTOON TAG

151

Calling all cartoons for a different kind of game.

There's only one way to make yourself "safe" when you play cartoon tag. You must drop to one knee and call out the name of a cartoon or cartoon character before you get tagged. If you don't call out something, or if you call out a cartoon that has already been named, and you get tagged, you're "it."

You can use any subject for this kind of tag: dogs, cats, states, boys' names, and so on.

MELTING TAG

Tag the players quickly, before they all melt!

If you are tagged, you must freeze in one place until you count to 100 by ones. You must stay in the same position—so if you're hands are up in the air when you're tagged, they must stay that way until you melt.

If you move before you melt, you are out of the game. As soon as you melt, get moving! When the person who is "it" freezes everyone, it's time to pick a new "it."

TUG-OF-WAR

It takes 2 to tug in this ancient test of strength.

You Will Need: An old beach towel

Roll up a beach towel (the long way) to make a "rope" for this tug-of-war. Each player holds onto one end of it. Stand far enough apart so the rope is stretched between you and the other player, then squat down. At the count of 3, start pulling, trying to force the other person to be the first to touch a hand to the ground or fall over. If you let go of the rope, you lose the game.

Sometimes a good strategy is to move your hands forward when the other person is pulling. It can throw your opponent off-balance!

ROOSTER CHASE

Move fast, or someone will grab your tail feathers!

You Will Need: Handkerchiefs or unfolded napkins, 1 for each player

The object of this game is to grab the handkerchief from the other player's back pocket. Before you begin, both players stuff the corner of a handkerchief into one of their back pockets so that most of the handkerchief sticks out. This is your "rooster tail."

Players must hop on one foot, holding the other leg at the ankle behind the back. On "Go," you must hop around, trying to grab the other player's rooster tail while protecting your own.

It's okay if you accidentally let go of your ankle, but if you touch that foot to the ground at any time, you lose the round.

SIMON SAYS—NOT

Sometimes it's important NOT to do what you're told!

Just in case you haven't played regular Simon Says in awhile, here are the basics. One person gets to be Simon. Players must obey everything Simon says, but only if Simon starts out with the words, "Simon says."

For example, if Simon calls out, "Simon says put your hands on your head," then everybody must obey. But if Simon calls out, "Clap your hands!" and you do, then you're out, because Simon didn't start out with "Simon says."

Simon Says—Not is a backward version of Simon Says. If Simon tells you, "Simon says touch your nose," you must do anything else but touch your nose. If you actually do what Simon says, you're out of the game. If Simon calls out, "Stick out your tongue!" without using the words "Simon says," then you must do exactly what Simon tells you.

156 HOP SNAILS

This hopscotch board looks like a snail's shell—but you'll have to be a lot quicker than a snail to win!

You Will Need: Chalk

Draw the spiral pattern on the ground, starting from the inside and working your way out. Number the squares as shown. Make the center circle about 1 foot wide. Decide who gets to hop first. He or she hops on ONE FOOT through all the boxes in order, starting with number 1, then jumps into the center circle on BOTH FEET. Then he or she hops on ONE FOOT back through the boxes to the beginning, hopping out on BOTH FEET.

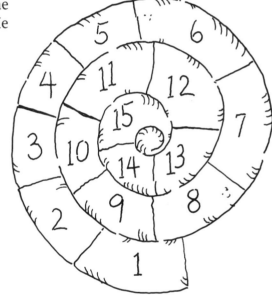

To finish, the player picks one of the boxes and writes his or her initials in it. From now on, no other player can hop in that box, but the player who owns that box MUST hop into it with BOTH FEET! The other players repeat the same steps on their turns, but they must be careful to jump OVER any boxes that have someone else's initials in them. The other players should watch the hoppers closely, because hoppers lose a turn if they:

— Step on a chalk line (numbers are okay)
— Hop on 1 foot when they should hop on 2
— Hop on 2 feet when they should hop on 1
— Hop into a box owned by another player

The game is over when all of the boxes have someone's initials in them. The person who owns the most boxes wins.

At the Restaurant

BACKWARD 20 QUESTIONS

157

Switch gears and challenge yourself to make a fun game even more fun by playing it in reverse!

If you've ever been "it" while playing the game 20 Questions, you know that you don't really get to say much. The other players take turns asking you yes-or-no questions and then try to guess what you're thinking about. But if you're "it" in Backward 20 Questions, you get to do most of the talking!

Tail large a has it.

First you must think of a person, place, or thing that the others will try to guess—for example, let's pretend you picked Barney the dinosaur. You must think of a hard clue to tell them about Barney. Don't make it too easy or they will guess right away. You might say, "I'm thinking of an animal that walks on its hind legs." (That's a good one, because lots of animals besides Barney walk on their hind legs.) The other players make one guess for every clue you give them.

Make each clue more specific without giving away your secret. Your next clue might be, "You can see this animal on television." If you give 20 clues without anyone guessing the right answer, you win. If someone else guesses your secret, that person wins and gets to be "it."

BUZZ!

Be your own buzzer, and turn on your number skills for this game!

In this game, everybody works together, taking turns counting to 100. Player 1 starts by saying "one," Player 2 then says "two," and so on. When all the players have said a number, keep going around again.

But here's the catch: If your number has a 7 in it (7, 17, 27, 37, and so on), or if it can be divided evenly by seven (7, 14, 21, 28, and so on), you must say "Buzz!" instead of saying the number. (Of course, you can pick any number you want.)

To make things really tricky, try playing Buzz with 2 numbers at a time. Say "Buzz!" for one number, and "Beep!" for the other. If our numbers were 5 and 8, for example, the game would sound something like this: 1, 2, 3, 4, Buzz, 6, 7, Beep, 9, Buzz, 11, 12, 13, 14, Buzz, Beep, 17, Beep, 19, Buzz, and so on.

TRAVEL TRIVIA

With an average elevation of only 100 feet, Louisiana is one of the lowest—and flattest—states. Much of its coastal area is actually below sea level, while its highest point, Driskill Mountain, reaches a height of only 535 feet.

MATH POTATO

Play Hot Potato with numbers, but be careful not to get "burned"!

In Hot Potato, players toss a potato or beanbag around in a circle while music is playing. The person who is holding the potato when the music stops is out of the game. Math Potato is a little different. In this game, you toss math problems back and forth as fast as you can. Here's how it works.

The first player starts by making up a simple math problem (such as 5+3). The next player must "toss" it to someone else by solving the problem and making a new problem out of the solution. For example, Player 1 says, "5 plus 3 equals____." Player 2 solves the problem by answering "8," then tosses it to Player 3 by saying, "8 minus 7 equals____." Player 3 solves the problem—"1"—then tosses it back to Player 1 by saying, "1 plus 13 equals____," and so on. Players who get the wrong answer to their problem are out until the next game.

COFFEEPOT

Can you coffeepot which word I'm thinking of?

Think of a verb (an action word) such as "walk." Then in your head, think of a sentence using that word. For example, "The tiger walks in the jungle." Say the sentence aloud for the other players, but replace your verb with the word "coffeepot." The sentence above would now become, "The tiger coffeepots in the jungle."

Now the other players must guess your word. If no one guesses correctly, think of a new sentence. "I walk to school everyday," for example, would be "I coffeepot to school everyday." Keep making up new sentences until someone guesses your word. The player who guesses your word gets to go next.

DON'T SAY IT!

Some letters are off-limits in this brain-bending definition game.

Choose a letter and say it aloud. (F, for example.) Another player then chooses any word. (Dog, for example.) Now it's your job to say a definition of that word. Easy, right? Everybody knows what a dog is. Dogs are animals that have four legs. They have fur all over their bodies. They are often called man's best friend. But here's the tricky part: Because you chose the letter F at the beginning of the game, you can't use the letter F in your definition! How in the world can you do it?

You can't say the word FOUR, but you can say, "A dog is an animal with three plus one legs." You can't say the word FUR, but you can say, "Dogs have hair all over their bodies." You can't say FRIEND, either, so a good sentence might be, "Some people call them, man's best pal."

Now it's your turn to try. Just remember what letter you choose—and don't say it!

COUNTING RACES

162

Here's an obstacle course for your mouth. Be careful not to trip over your tongue!

For each of the following rounds, have someone time how far you can get in 30 seconds. Write down where you finished. Then let other players try.

Round 1: Count backward from 100 as fast as you can.
Round 2: Count forward by 2s.
Round 3: Count forward by 7s. (Getting tough yet?)
Round 4: This one is tricky. Count backward by 3s, starting at 100.
Round 5: WARNING: Play this round only if you like to sweat! Starting at 100, count backward once by 8, and then add 5. Repeat.

As with a real obstacle course, you'll be amazed to see how your time improves the more you play. Can you think of more counting races to play?

I KNEW A SPY

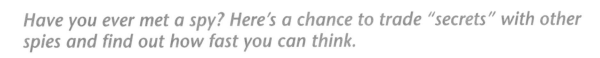

163

Have you ever met a spy? Here's a chance to trade "secrets" with other spies and find out how fast you can think.

Starting with the first letter of the alphabet, players must think of a first name, a last name, and a profession that begins with that letter. For example, Player 1 might begin with "I knew a person named Albert Adams. Everyone thought he was an Airplane pilot, but secretly he was a spy!"

Player 2 might say, "I knew a person named Barbara Benson. Everyone thought she was a Baker, but really she was a spy!" Players work their way through the alphabet. If you can't think of the 3 words for a letter, then you lose a turn and the next player gets to try.

SLINGING PHRASES

164

Test your memory with this sentence-building game.

Player 1 begins by saying a short, simple sentence. The next player repeats the sentence and adds a short phrase. Players keep slinging the sentence back and forth by repeating it and then adding something else.

For example, Player 1 begins by saying, "The cat chased the rat." The next player says, "The cat chased the rat down the alley." The next player says, "The cat chased the rat down the alley behind the building," and so on, until someone forgets part of the sentence. It's easier to remember the sentence if you keep the phrases short. You might want to have a rule that you can't add more than 4 or 5 words during your turn.

BACKWARD ALPHABET

165

If you think walking backward is tough, try talking backward!

Saying the alphabet is easy, right? You've probably been doing it since kindergarten. But saying it backward is a lot harder, even though you know all the letters by heart.

First, have somebody time you as you say the alphabet forward from A to Z. How long did it take you? 15 seconds? 10 seconds? Now put yourself in reverse and say it from Z to A. Have someone time you again. Try it several times in a row to see if your time improves. Who has the fastest time?

UNEM A TEG

166

What? You say the words don't make sense? Try them backward.

You Will Need: Restaurant menu

Pick a word off the menu and say it backward. Have the people at your table guess what you're trying to say. You can give them some clues, if you like. For example, you can say, "I'd like a cup of eeffoc today." Just be careful not to order your food backward! Who knows what could happen!

WORD WEBBING

Play this game with someone who always wants to have the last word!

This game is similar to Slinging Phrases (#102), but here the object is to build a sentence one word at a time. Player 1 starts out by saying a word that could be the beginning of a sentence. The next player says that word and adds another word.

For example, Player 1 says, "The." Player 2 says, "The cow." Player 3 says, "The cow ran," and so on. (The only rule is that every word you add must help make a sentence. For example, Player 3 could not add the word "green" or "airplane" because neither "The cow green" nor "The cow airplane" can be made into a real sentence.) How many words can you web together into one sentence?

168 ALPHAGORIES

Play this game with Tina, Tonya, Tammy, Thelma, Tess, Tiffany, and Tracy and their friends Tom, Tim, Ted, Theo, Terry and Todd.

One player calls out a category—girls' names, for example. Somebody else calls out a letter, such as "T." Players then take turns thinking of girls' names that begin with "T." Play ends when no one can think of another word in the category.

Here are a few other categories you can choose: animals, fruits, cereal brands, vegetables, cartoon characters, state names, plants, colors, cars, book titles. How many more can you think of?

SIGNS OF MEMORY 169

This game will have you laughing so hard that it'll be hard to concentrate!

Player 1 starts out by making a facial expression or hand gesture. The next player must repeat the movement and add one of his own. Keep going around the group, repeating movements and adding new ones, until someone forgets a movement—or until everyone breaks up laughing!

For example, you can blink your eyes, bear your teeth, pull your ear, scratch your hand, pat your cheek, stick out your tongue, and so on.

170 RHYME TIME

Cow, plow, wow, sow, brow, chow, now, how...

One player begins the game by saying any word. The next person must say a word that rhymes with it. Keep going until you can't think of another word. Players can pass if they can't think of any more.

If you want to keep score, give 1 point for each word rhymed. If you want to score as a group, time yourselves. See how many words you can think of in the shortest length of time. You'll be surprised at how many rhymes you can find.

ANTONYM ANTS

171

Pretend you're on a picnic, eating words. But you'll have to pick the ants out of your sentences first!

Antonyms are pairs of words that mean the opposite of each other, such as hot and cold, day and night, big and small. The object of this game is for one player to pick the "ant" (antonym) out of a sentence and give its opposite back to the first player.

For example, Player 1 thinks of a sentence that has an antonym in it, such as "The soup is hot." Player 2 then finds the word in the sentence that has an antonym: HOT. Player 2 takes the antonym of HOT and works it into the sentence, adding a new antonym at the end. For example, Player 2 says, "The soup is HOT, but the water in the pool is COLD and SHALLOW."

Player 1 in turn finds the new "ant" (SHALLOW) and returns a new sentence using that word. A game might go something like this:

Player 1: The soup is HOT.
Player 2: The soup is hot, but the water in the pool is COLD and SHALLOW.
Player 1: The water in the pool is shallow, but the river is DEEP and WIDE.
Player 2: The river is wide, but the hallway is NARROW and LONG.
Player 1: The hallway is long, but Santa Claus is SHORT and FAT.
Player 2: Santa Claus is fat, but the toothpick is SKINNY and. . . .

See how long you can keep the "ants" moving in your word picnic!

DEFEND YOURSELF

Order in the court! Order in the court! Can you defend yourself to the judge and jury?

> Michael Jordan is like a bird because...

Pick one player to be "it." This player silently thinks of a real person or a character from a book, TV show, or movie. (Try to think of someone whom everyone knows.) For example, Michael Jordan. Remember, don't say it out loud yet!

The other player says, "Your person is like a _____", filling in the blank with a noun. For example, "Your person is like a bird."

The person who is "it" must then say his or her person out loud and defend it by thinking of why the person he or she thought of is like a bird. For example, he might say, "Michael Jordan is like a bird because he really flies through the air when he plays basketball!"

VERBAL HOT POTATO

Here's a variation on Hot Potato with words that just might burn your tongue if you don't shout them out fast enough!

The first player makes a "hot potato word" by saying a 3-letter word. The next player must take the letters from that word and shout 3 new words using the letters in the "hot potato word."

For example, if the first player says, "Dog!" then the next player says, "Dig Oats Green!" as fast as he or she can. The next player says, "Dime Open Girl!" and so on, until someone messes up. Then it's up to the next player to come up with a new "hot potato word."

Special Rule: Once a word is used, nobody else can use that word until the next round.

STRAW WORMS

174

All you need is a restaurant straw to make this wiggly, jiggly paper worm!

You Will Need: Drinking straw with wrapper still on it, water

Hold a drinking straw by one end. With your other hand, scrunch down the paper slowly, working from the top down. Don't let the paper slip off the straw. When you get the paper near the bottom, scrunch it down as tight as you can get it. The tighter you scrunch, the wigglier your worm will be!

Slip the wrapper off the straw, and lay the wrapper down on the table on its side. Dip the straw in some water. Before you take the straw out, put your finger over the end of the straw and trap some water inside. Now drip a little bit of water from the straw onto the wrapper. If you have scrunched it up tight enough, you won't believe what happens next! Keep dripping water on it until the entire wrapper is wet.

MAGIC STRAW

175

With a mysterious wave of your hand, you can make a drinking straw move by itself!

You Will Need: 1 round drinking straw

First, address your audience: "Drinking straws are very shy creatures. But if I slowly wave my hand over one, I can convince it to move by itself. Watch!" Wave your hand over the straw, saying things like, "Come on, you can do it! I know you can!" You can even tap the table underneath the straw, or trace a big circle around the straw with your index finger, as you continue to talk to it: "Roll over! Go on, you can do it!" Sure enough, the drinking straw rolls slowly away from you—and you haven't touched it once!

How do you do it? Easy. The straw moves because you are gently blowing on it! First you have to distract your audience. To do that, you have to make them look at your hands and the straw, not at your face. That's why it's important to keep your hands moving as much as possible. Also, don't simply pucker your lips and blow. Instead, open your lips slightly, blowing at the straw forcefully, but without making any sound. It's easy once you get the hang of it, but practice first.

THE MINISTER'S CAT

176

The minister's cat sure has a crazy personality!

Player 1 starts the game by saying, "The minister's cat is_____." Fill in the blank with a word that begins with the letter A. The next player repeats the sentence and adds a word that begins with the letter B, and so on, until someone forgets a word or you reach the end of the alphabet. For example:

"The minister's cat is aggressive."
"The minister's cat is aggressive and bashful."
"The minister's cat is aggressive and bashful and curious."

TRAVEL TRIVIA

Charleston, South Carolina, boasts America's first museum and first real theater. Our first opera and symphony orchestra were heard there as well.

NAME DROPPING

177

Have you ever been invited to a Hollywood party?

Players pretend that they went to a fabulous party the night before, and then tell each other who they saw there, starting with the letter A and going to Z. The first player starts by thinking of a name and an adjective that begins with the letter A. For example, "I went to a party last night and met Adorable Adam."

The next player repeats that name and adds another person and adjective that begins with the letter B. For example, "I went to a party last night and met Adorable Adam and Bashful Betty." With each new turn, the next player must repeat all the names already mentioned and then add the next letter of the alphabet.

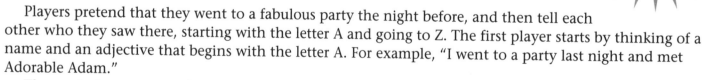

At the Hotel

178

ROYAL CHECKERS

Is there any place safe to hide?

You Will Need: Checkerboard and pieces created before the trip (see #6)

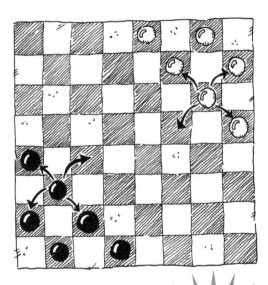

Set up the game as shown. The first player to capture all of the opponent's pieces wins. All pieces play on the same color squares.

In Royal Checkers, every playing piece is like a "king." That means all pieces can be moved forward or backward, as long as they stay on the same color. Watch for multiple jump opportunities. You are allowed to jump over your own pieces if they are in spaces next to you.

SHOO FLY

179

Here is another version of 20 Questions that is best played indoors.

The player who is "it" chooses a specific spot in the room (a certain place on a wall, on top of a piece of furniture, etc.). That person then imagines that he or she is a housefly on that chosen spot. He or she must imagine the view of the room that the fly would have from that spot.

The other players try to find the fly by asking yes-or-no questions about what it can or can't see. For example, "Can you see the door from where you are?" would be one type of question to ask. The other players can make 1 guess for each question asked. If the person who is the housefly gives 10 answers without anyone figuring out where he or she is hiding, the fly wins. If someone does find the fly, that person wins—and gets to be "it" next.

SLAPJACK

You'll need quick hands and a quick eye to capture all the cards!

You Will Need: A deck of cards

Slapjack is sort of like the card game War, but with a louder bang. Deal out all the cards, one at a time. Players hold their cards in one hand, face down. Everybody turns over one card at the same time, tossing it into the center. Whenever a jack or a queen turns up, try to slap your hand down on top of it. The first player to slap the queen or jack gets to pick up the pile. Put captured cards aside until later.

Pick up your captured cards whenever you run out of cards in your hand. If you run out of cards completely, you lose the game.

TRAVEL TRIVIA
Nevada is the driest state and one of the hottest. It is also one of the wealthiest states in terms of individual income.

SLUGFEST

Battle it out in this 2-player winner-take-all card game.

You Will Need: A deck of cards

A full deck of cards is dealt between 2 players (26 cards each). Each player turns over his or her top card at the same time. The player with the higher card gets to take the other player's card "prisoner." (If you both turn up the same card at the same time, each of you must flip over another card and compare them. The high card captures both of the other player's cards.)

Keep playing until you run out of cards, then shuffle your captured cards and use those. Beware of aces. When a player turns up an ace during the course of the game, he or she automatically gives the ace and 5 cards (from the top of the deck) to the other player. These are added to the other player's "capture" pile. The player who captures all the cards is the winner!

SILLY SIXES

If you're tired of playing Crazy Eights, try this twist!

You Will Need: A deck of cards

Silly Sixes is played just like the popular Crazy Eights, except that 6s and 7s have special powers. Every time you lay down a 6, players have to trade cards with the person to their left. Every time you lay down a 7, the turns reverse and you start playing in the opposite direction.

If you don't know how to play Crazy Eights, here are the rules: Deal out 8 cards to each player. Put the deck in the center and turn 1 card up. This is the discard pile. Start with the player to the left of the dealer. If a player has a card that matches the number or suit of the card on top of the discard pile, the player lays that card down on the pile. For example, if the card on the pile is a 4 of hearts, you can lay down any heart card or any 4 card. If you don't have a matching card, you must draw 1 card from the deck and then pass your turn.

If you have an 8, you can lay it down on the pile and call out a suit (hearts, clubs, diamonds, or spades). This changes the suit of the pile. If you have a handful of hearts, for example, but everybody else keeps playing diamonds and spades, you can lay down the 8, call "Hearts!" and automatically change the suit. NOTE: The person after you can lay down an 8, too, and change the suit to something else. Watch out!

TRAVEL TRIVIA

Even with its 20 museums—several of which are located along the National Mall in Washington, D.C.—the Smithsonian Institution has room to display only about one percent of its 137 million catalogued items.

CHUMP CHECKERS

When does a loser become a winner?

Hurray!
I lost again!

You Will Need: Checkerboard and pieces created before the trip (see #6)

Chump Checkers is played just like regular checkers, with one big difference: The first player to lose all of his or her pieces wins the game! The object of the game is to place your pieces where your opponent can capture (jump over) them. All pieces play on the same color squares.

There are 2 special rules. First, you must always capture your opponent's pieces, if you can. You cannot intentionally avoid multiple jumps. Also, you do not get a "king" if you reach the opposite side of the board. Instead, you must turn around and come back in the direction you came.

SOUND EFFECT CHARADES

In this charades game, the people who are guessing have to close their eyes—so it's best if the driver doesn't play!

Divide into 2 teams. Each team writes a noun or verb on a piece of paper for the other team, then each team picks 1 person to be its charade maker. This person is shown the word the other team has chosen, which he or she must now act out for his or her own team members to guess.

The trick is that the charade maker can only use sound effects—no words or hand motions. Just to be sure, the other members of his or her team must close their eyes. The charade maker can use any nearby objects or body parts to make the sound effect. For example, if the word on the paper was CAR, the charade maker could make a honking noise. If the word was RUNNING, he or she could run in place.

Use a watch to time each charade. The team that can guess the most words in the least amount of time wins the game.

TABLETOP FOOTBALL

185

After folding a piece of paper into a "football" triangle, you can play a surprisingly fun game of football.

You Will Need: 1 sheet of paper

To make the football, fold a piece of paper in half lengthwise, then fold it in half again (Picture 1). Starting from the bottom, fold the corner up to the right (Picture 2). Then fold the bottom up (Picture 3). Repeat this folding back and forth. At the top, tuck the flap of paper back into the triangle (Picture 4). Now you're ready to play!

Sit across from each other at a table. One player is the kicker. The other player makes a goalpost with his or her hands by holding the thumbs together, with pointer fingers sticking straight up (Picture 5).

The kicker puts one point of the football against the table and holds it there with his pointer finger (Picture 6). Using the other pointer finger, he or she flicks the bottom of the football and tries to get it to fly between the goalposts. A player gets 2 tries to make it, scoring 1 point for each successful kick. Then it's the other player's turn.

As you get better with Tabletop Football, try playing across a longer "playing field" such as a picnic table or a hotel bed.

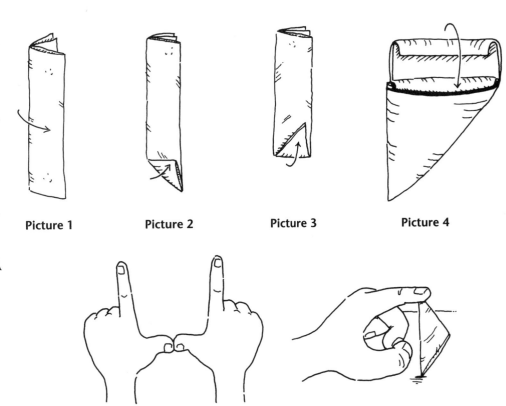

Picture 1 **Picture 2** **Picture 3** **Picture 4**

Picture 5 **Picture 6**

CAT & DOGS

186

Can the cunning cat escape the dogged dogs?

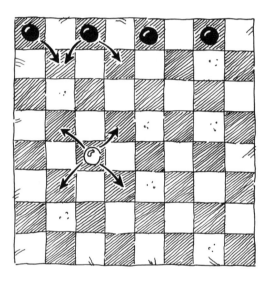

You Will Need: Checkerboard and pieces created before the trip (see #6)

The cat wins the game if it can break through the line of dogs and reach the opposite side. The dogs win the game if they can trap the cat so it cannot move.

To start the game, the player with the "dogs" puts them on the 4 playing squares in the first row, as shown. The player with the "cat" can put a checker anywhere he or she wants, as long as it is on the same color square as the dogs. The dogs can only move forward diagonally 1 square at a time, just like regular checkers. The cat can move forward or backward, 1 square at a time. There is no capturing in this game, so the cat cannot jump over the dogs.

AND THEN WHAT?

187

Plenty happens between waking up and going to sleep!

When you're traveling, you discover so many new sights and sounds that it's easy to forget some of them. You can help out your memory by taking time to remember a few highlights out of each day. Before you go to bed, think about what happened since you woke up that morning. Talk about it with the people you're traveling with, or just think about it in your head.

When did you get up? What did you wear? What did you eat for breakfast? Who did you see? Where did you go? How did you get there? Try to remember as many details as you can—your memories are sure to last longer that way! See who in your family can remember the most things that happened during the day.

FLOATING TO SLEEP

Getting to sleep can be tough sometimes—especially after a long day of traveling. Here's an activity that will help.

When you need the Sandman to visit and bring you some dreams, try "floating to sleep." First, get as comfortable as you can, then take a deep breath and slowly let it out.

Next, think about your feet. Imagine that they are as light as marshmallows bobbing in warm chocolate. Concentrate on how your feet feel against the sheets. Imagine that they are sinking into an ocean of pudding. Suddenly, you realize that you can't move them, so you start thinking about your legs, which feel like 2 branches floating in a quiet stream; and your back, which relaxes 1 inch at a time, like a sheet falling gently on the bed; and your arms, which are resting on fluffy clouds made of cotton and feathers and warm air.

By the time you get to your neck and head, you should feel pretty comfortable. You don't have to move at all, because the Sandman is just around the corner, bringing you dreams to last all night long.

TRAVEL TRIVIA

Carlsbad Caverns National Park, in New Mexico, is where you'll find the Big Room, the largest known underground chamber in the Western Hemisphere. It is 1,800 feet long and up to 1,100 feet wide—and tall enough to contain a 30-story building.

MAKING WISHES

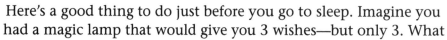

189

Rub the magic lamp and get 3 wishes!

Here's a good thing to do just before you go to sleep. Imagine you had a magic lamp that would give you 3 wishes—but only 3. What would you wish for? (No fair wishing for more wishes!) Would you use all 3 wishes at once, or would you save them for later?

Imagine that you had 3 wishes that you could use only for other people, not for yourself. Now what would you wish for? Would you wish for something for your mom or dad? Your brother or sister? Your best friend? Or maybe for someone you never met before in your life?

PENNY DARTS

190

These darts don't have sharp points, but you can still make a bull's-eye!

You Will Need: Sheet of notebook-sized paper, pennies, pencil or crayon

Draw a target as big as you can on a sheet of paper, then lay the target on the floor. Walk 3 big steps away from it, and mark a throwing line. Each player takes turns tossing 3 pennies onto the target from behind the throwing line. Keep score by adding up the number of points each player gets during his or her turn. If a penny misses the paper, no points are given. If the penny lands on a line between 2 circles, the player scores the higher number. Play until somebody reaches 50 points—or whatever number you choose.

CARD TOSS

The object of this game is to toss playing cards so that they land on the targets that you create.

You Will Need: 4 sheets of notebook-size paper (folded newspaper work well, too), playing cards

Arrange the sheets of paper on the ground in whatever pattern you choose, just as long as they are not touching each other. Decide where players will stand when they toss their cards. This is the throwing line, and no player may cross it while throwing cards.

On each target, write the number of points that each target is worth. Make the targets that are farther away from the throwing line worth more points than the targets that are closer. Take turns, each player tossing 1 card at a time, to see who can land the most cards on the targets. The player with the most points after all 52 cards have been tossed wins.

HIDE THE FISH

Once you've been fished, you never forget it!

You Will Need: Paper, pencil

This game can take days to play—being sneaky is the toughest part. First, make your fish by taking small strips of paper and drawing a fish on each one, as shown. On the back of each fish, write your initials. Each person playing should make the same number of fish. A dozen or so is a good number.

Whenever you get a chance, hide your fish in and around different places. Put one in the glove compartment box, one in somebody's shoe, another in somebody's shirt pocket or suitcase, perhaps one in between the pages of a book—wherever you think somebody else will find it later during your trip.

If someone catches you hiding a fish, you must tear that fish up and throw it away. That's why it's important to be sneaky! Each time you find somebody else's fish (you'll know by the initials on the back), save it. At the end of your trip, see who was the best fisherman (the person who found the most fish), and who was best at hiding them (the person who had the least number of his or her fish found).

TRAVEL TRIVIA
The only living coral reefs in the continental United States are located in Southern Florida's Biscayne National Park. The 173,000-acre park is also home to manatees, sea turtles, sharks, eagles, and many species of tropical birds.

MIRROR

The object of this game is to "mirror" another person—as closely as possible.

Stand so that you and a partner are 4 feet apart and able to see each other very well. Decide before you begin who will be the Mirror. When the other person slowly moves a part of his or her body—arm, hand, leg, eyebrows, mouth—it is up to the Mirror to move in exactly the same way, just as your reflection would move in a real mirror. Gradually speed up your movements. How long can the Mirror keep up with the person making the movements? After a while, switch roles.

FLASHLIGHT FIND

What will the searchlight uncover next?

You Will Need: Flashlight

Here's a nighttime game that's great for hotel rooms. While everyone else is out of the room, one person hides something small from view. Then, with all the lights out, the other players take turns pointing the beam of a flashlight around the room, trying to find the object. When the light is moving closer to the hidden object, the person who hid it should say "Brighter!" If the light is moving away from the hidden object, the person should say "Darker!" Whoever finds the hidden object gets to hide it someplace else next.

I REMEMBER

Can you remember all the places you have visited?

Each player thinks of a place that the family has visited together. Take turns describing the place, 1 clue at a time, until someone guesses. For example, if you are thinking about the amusement park you visited 2 years ago, you could start out by saying, "I remember the day was very hot." Try not to make the clues too easy.

HOTEL SCAVENGER HUNT

196

How many of these things can you spy in your hotel room?

Here are a list of items found in most hotel rooms around the country. Next to it is the number of points each item is worth. Count how many of them you find—don't take them with you, just spy them out!—and add up your total points.

alarm clock (1)

bible (2)

bottle opener (3)

business card (4)

coffeepot (2)

drinking glass (1)

extra pillow (1)

facial tissues (1)

hair dryer (4)

hand soap (1)

hanger (1)

hotel brochure (3)

ice bucket (1)

iron (5)

magazine (4)

mint (6)

pen (2)

postcard (4)

refrigerator (4)

menu (1)

shampoo (2)

stationery (3)

telephone book (1)

TV directory (1)

RECYCLER

197

Use the game board you made in Chapter 1 to play this portable game that's never the same twice.

You Will Need: Recycler game board pieces (#20), 1 die or spinner (See #1 for directions on making one), several coins or other objects that can be used as markers

Remove the "Start" and "Finish" cards from your deck of game board pieces. Shuffle the rest, and lay them down one by one in whatever shape you want, one after the other. Put the "Start" card at the beginning and the "Finish" card at the end. Now you're ready to begin.

Each player uses a coin or other marker to show where he or she is during the game. Roll the die or use a spinner to see how many spaces each person should move during each turn. Players race to see who can make it to the "Finish" first using the directions laid out. If you land on a blank card, don't do anything. When the game is over, shuffle the cards and start again. It's different every time!

If you can defend the person you chose, you score 1 point. If you can't, you score no points. Players take turns. The first person to score 10 points wins the game.

MAKING TENTS

You can "camp out" even if you are staying in a hotel room!

You Will Need: Blankets, chair or table

The goal is to make a tent by covering a table or chairs with a blanket. You can simply throw a blanket over the table, but it's more fun to make unusual tent shapes.

For example, put 2 chairs front to front and cover them with a blanket. Crawl under and sit on the seats. Pretend you are in a spaceship on the way to the moon! You can also crawl under the chairs and pretend you are in a tunnel far beneath the surface of the earth. Or you can put the 2 chairs next to a table and cover them all with blankets. Pretend you have just built an igloo in the far north. Crawl under the chairs to get inside your igloo. Make a secret knock that people must use before they can come in.

What other fun tents can you make?

SHUFFLEPENNY

The closer you get to the edge, the better!

You Will Need: 3 pennies for each player, a smooth, flat table

The object of Shufflepenny is to get your penny as close to the edge of the table without falling off. Players take turns sliding 1 penny at a time across the table, trying to get as close to the edge as possible. Start from one side of the table and slide toward the opposite side.

You can hit one of your own pennies with another penny and try to "bump" it closer to the edge of the table, but if you knock your own penny off the table, that penny is out of the game. You can also try to bump other players' pennies out of the way with your penny. But if any of your pennies fall off the table during your turn, these pennies are out.

If someone else bumps one of your coins off the surface during their turn, you can pick it up and start playing again on your next turn at the original starting line. Once the game has started, you can't move your coins off the playing surface.

TREASURE MAP

Bury a treasure, matey, and leave clues that reveal its secret location!

You Will Need: Paper, pencil

Hide something small in your hotel room, such as a piece of candy or small toy that you want to give away. Next, create a series of notes that people will have to find in order to discover your treasure. On each note, write a clue that leads to the next note.

On the first note, for example, you might write, "Look in something that holds water." Give this note to the finder to start the game. The finder looks in the tub and finds a note that you wrote that says, "Look behind your backward self."

After thinking for a bit, the finder guesses that the next note is behind the mirror. The note there reads, "Look in something that protects your feet," which leads to a note hidden in a sock, and so on, until the last note, which tells the person where to find the hidden treasure.

After all that work, it's better to let the finder keep the treasure, so make sure you hide something you don't mind giving away! Leave as many clues as you want—just make sure that they eventually lead back to the object you want them to find!

REVERSE IT

201

Don't let your opponent capture your colors!

You Will Need: 64 playing pieces (black on one side, white on the other), standard checkerboard or the one you made in Chapter 1 (see #6).

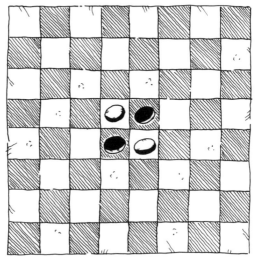

Picture 1

Picture 2

The object of this game is to be the player with the most pieces of your chosen color (black or white) faceup on the board at the end of the game. Each player starts off with 32 pieces of one color or the other. The idea is to trap the other player's pieces between 2 of your pieces, thereby making them your own. When a white piece is trapped between 2 black pieces, for example, the white piece is "captured" and turned over so the black side shows up.

Begin by placing 4 playing pieces—2 from each player—in the starting pattern as shown in Picture 1, then take turns placing additional playing pieces of your color on the board. Try to trap at least 1 of the opponent's pieces between 2 of your own (in a straight or diagonal direction). If you can't make any move, as sometimes happens, you lose a turn.

Note that any piece may be turned over many different times during the game as it is captured and recaptured. It is also possible to capture several pieces at once if they are lined up properly. (See what happens in Picture 2 if you put a white game piece in the square marked with the letter W.)

Pieces are never removed from the board. The game ends when all the squares on the board are covered and both players have no pieces left.

MAZES & PUZZLES

Mazes and puzzles come in many different forms, as you are about to see. The games and activities in this chapter include classic brainteasers, simple word puzzles, riddles of all kinds, question-and-answer games, visual challenges, and various other exercises that, while they are designed to be fun, also test one's ability to solve problems. Several of the activities are best played by a group, but the majority are geared toward the individual player. Still, there's something here for every age group—and even a few activities that grown-ups can take part in.

CHALKBOARD REBUS

In a rebus, you read pictures as if they were words. Can you figure out the rebus below? (Answers on page 233.)

Dear Class,

Your T+ can  at today. H+ is

your assignment. Please it in +4 three o' . Write a

story about a  , a , and a  +ger.

RECYCLED MAZE

203

Like the game Recycler (#197), this maze is different each time you play it.

You Will Need: 30 pieces of thin cardboard or heavy paper cut into 2-inch squares (or better yet, use the backs of the same pieces you used for the Recycler game), markers or crayons

Copy the designs provided onto each card. All the lines should begin and end in the center of the edges. That way, all the lines will match up when the cards are laid next to each other. To play, shuffle the cards and lay them out 1 by 1 into 5 rows of 6 cards. Use your finger to connect the "Start" card and the "Finish" card, wherever they may be. Some of the mazes you create will be simple, some hard, some impossible. Time yourself!

THE STATE OF AEIOU

204

Someone has taken all the consonants and left only the vowels in the list of states below! Can you figure out the state names? We've done the first one for you. (Answers on page 233.)

1. I _ _ I A _ A   INDIANA
2. O _ E _ O _
3. A _ A _ A _ A
4. _ I _ _ I _ _ I _ _ I
5. _ A _ I _ O _ _ I A
6. _ E _ A _
7. _ E _ _ E _ _ EE
8. _ AI _ E
9. _ E _ _ O _ _
10. _ I _ _ I _ IA
11. O _ _ A _ O _ A
12. A _ I _ O _ A
13. _ _ O _ I _ A
14. _ E _ _ U _ _ _
15. _ EO _ _ IA
16. _ O _ _ E _ _ I _ U _
17. I _ A _ O
18. _ O _ _ A _ A
19. _ E _ _ A _ _ A
20. I _ _ I _ OI _

CAVE MAZE

In this finger maze, help the poor bear find its way to the mouth of the cave.

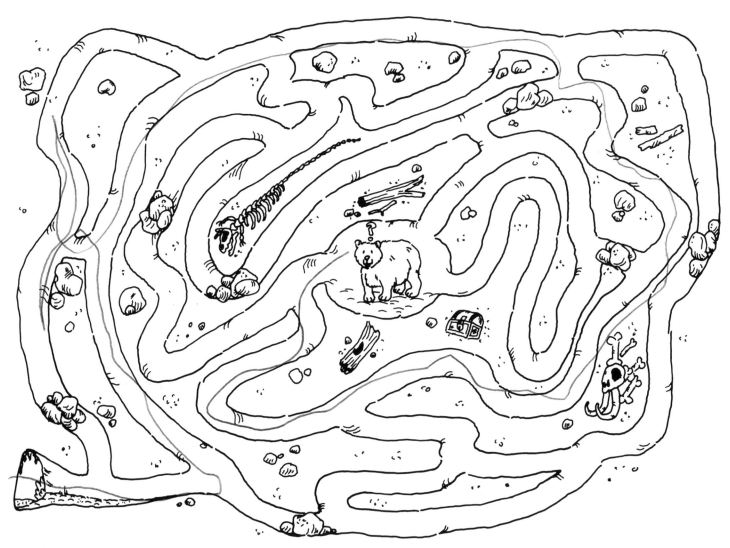

MYSTERY IN CHINA

Can you solve your way out of this mystery?

While traveling in China, you get into a tournament with the Chinese national Ping-Pong champion. The gym you're playing in is packed with people, and he's the best in the world. You're nervous, but all you need is 1 more point to beat him! On your final serve, you slam the ball so hard it misses the table, hits the ceiling, bounces on the floor, and rolls into a small drain that someone left uncovered in the corner. Unfortunately, it's the only ball you have.

"Who left this drain uncovered?" you ask. "The plumber," says the Ping-Pong champion. "The drain is clogged, so we called him to fix it. He went to get a special tool, and he won't be back for hours." You can see the Ping-Pong ball way down the drain, about 8 inches out of your reach. You must get the ball out quickly so you can try to win the tournament. The crowd in the bleachers won't wait long.

The only objects available to you are 2 Ping-Pong paddles, a small hand towel, 2 pitchers of water, 2 cups, and a stack of Ping-Pong rulebooks. How will you get the Ping-Pong ball? (Give up? See page 234.)

TRAVEL TRIVIA
The geographic center of North America is near Rugby, North Dakota. The geographic center of the United States is near Castle Rock, South Dakota.

WHO AM I?

Have you ever forgotten your own name? You will when you play this guessing game!

Think of a person or character. Pick someone that other players will probably know. We'll use Snow White in our example. The other player will try to guess the person you have chosen. He or she asks, "Who Am I?" You respond by giving clues, one at a time. After each clue, the other person tries to guess the secret identity. Clues for Snow White might be:

1. You have black hair and live in the forest.
2. One of your friends is always in a bad mood. (Grumpy)
3. You get very sleepy after eating an apple.

Keep going until the person who is guessing gets the right answer. To keep score, count the questions and see how long it takes a player to figure out "Who Am I?"

POSTCARD JIGSAW

Make this "puzzling" message and send it to a friend.

You Will Need: Postcards (larger ones work best), pencil, scissors

Write a note to your friend on the back of a postcard. Use the whole back if you want, even the part where you're supposed to put the address. Next, draw a jigsaw pattern on the back of the postcard. Make sure that the pieces are different shapes and sizes, but don't make the pieces too small because it might be too tough to cut them out. Now carefully cut out your pattern to make a mini-puzzle out of your postcard.

Put the pieces of the puzzle into an envelope, and mail them to a friend to figure out. He or she will have to put the puzzle together to read your message! For more of a challenge, make jigsaw puzzles out of several postcards that are the same size and mix them together before mailing them.

VOLCANO MAZE

Help the scientist get down the mountain to his helicopter without crossing the lava flow.

SCRAMBLERS

210

Sorting out a scrambled puzzle takes real word muscle.

Unscramble the following words, and write them down on a separate piece of paper. Then, circle individual letters in each word as instructed. Finally, use all of the circled letters to figure out the 2-word answer to the following riddle: What has 4 wheels and flies? (Answers on page 234.)

P R A T
(Circle first 3 letters.)

I G L E G G
(Circle third, fourth, and sixth letters.)

C R A B E
(Circle first 3 letters.)

C U L K Y
(Circle middle 3 letters.)

Making your own scramblers for other people is just as much fun as solving them yourself. It is easiest if you work backward and think of the riddle you want to solve first. Write the answer down, then think of some short words that have those letters in them. Scramble the words and you're done!

TRAVEL TRIVIA

The longest covered bridge in the United States spans the Connecticut River at the town of Windsor, Connecticut. Measuring 337 feet, it is longer than a football field.

LINE TRACE #1

211

Here's a picture that was made with one long line. The artist never picked up the pen when drawing it. Follow the line with your finger. Can you find the end of the line?

STATE MATCH

Can you match the name of the state with its shape?

Sound easy? Well, you'd better be careful—some of the states are shown sideways, upside-down, or even reversed, as if you were seeing them in a mirror! (Answers on page 234.)

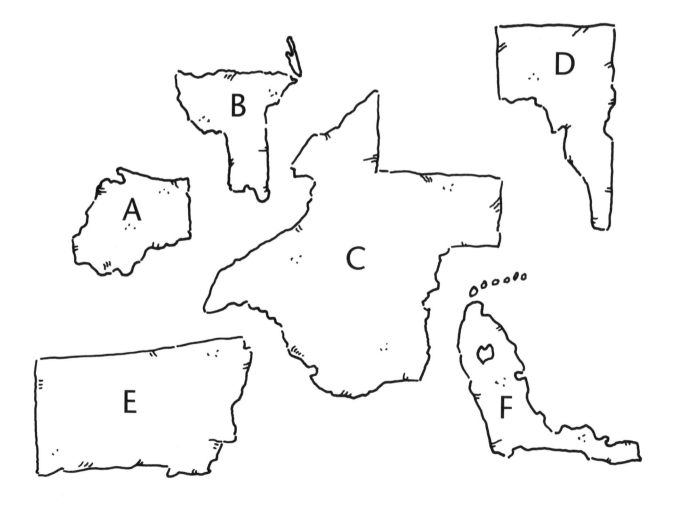

ROUNDABOUT

Don't get dizzy spinning your eyes around these puzzles!

Look carefully at these circular word puzzles. If you move from the outside in, you can spell 3-letter words using the letters in the circles. But some of the letters are missing! Can you figure out which letters they should be? Write down all the words they make. (Answers on page 234.)

Try making your own circle puzzles by drawing the circles and lines on another piece of paper as you see them here. Then fill in all the boxes with different letters to make your own words. Erase the letters from the middle ring and see if someone else can solve your circle puzzle. HINT: If you want to make it really tricky, erase the letters from the middle ring and the center ring, leaving only the outer ring filled in.

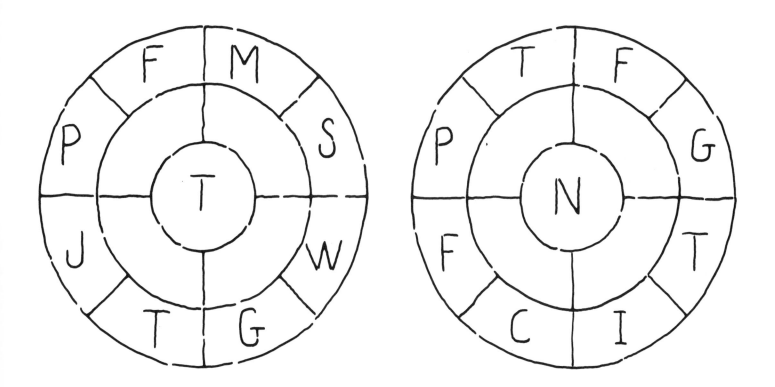

MEGA MATCHUP

How quickly can you find the 3 pairs of matching squares in this puzzle? Careful, some squares are turned sideways. (Answers on page 234.)

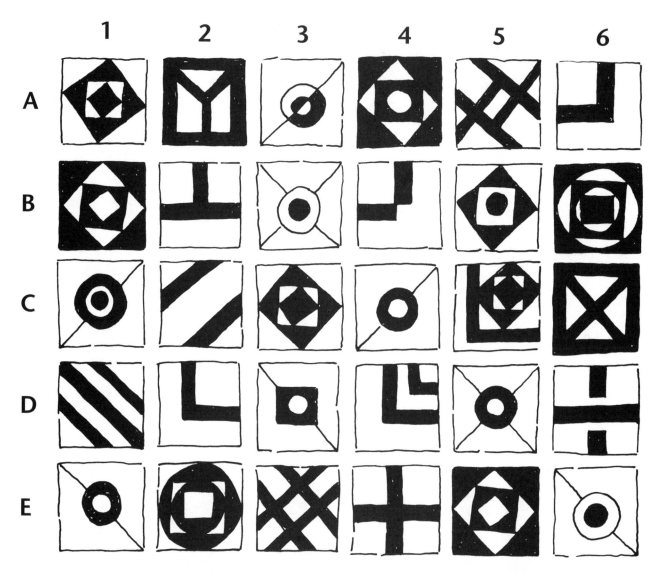

CAVEMAN REBUS

215

Can you figure out the rebus below? (Answers on page 234.)

Thousands of Y+s ago, +4 s and s were

invented,  used s and s to kill their prey. They

cooked their 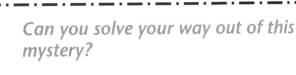s over a big .

MYSTERY IN ENGLAND

216

Can you solve your way out of this mystery?

While visiting your uncle, Lord Wisenberry of Eaglethorpe, in his English mansion, you decide to go exploring. In the basement, you accidentally lock yourself in a dusty storage room. There's only 1 door and no windows. The door key is hanging on a hook high on the wall, but no matter how much you jump, you can't reach it, and there are no windows. You try calling for help, but everyone is at the other end of the mansion.

The only items in the room are a deck of playing cards with the king of spades missing, a broken cardboard box holding a set of 24 encyclopedias from 1934, and a dirty blue rug. How will you get out of the room? (Give up? See page 234.)

AVALANCHE MAZE

Follow the path of footprints in this finger maze to help the mapmaker get to the cabin. Watch out for false leads!

SPACE SHUTTLE MYSTERY

218

Can you solve your way way out of this mystery?

You are the captain of the U.S.S. *Constitution*, the country's newest space shuttle. It's your last day in orbit around the earth. After checking to make sure all systems are "Go," you line up the space vehicle with a nearby space station, where you will re-fuel for your journey back to Earth.

The space station's flight engineer directs you to a special docking bay where you are instructed to land. But when you get there, you realize that something is wrong. The space shuttle is too wide to get through the docking bay's doorway! After measuring the opening, you determine that it is exactly 4 inches too narrow.

You have to land the shuttle soon because your fuel supply is running low. The docking bay's door is made of strong metal, so you can't cut it. And you certainly can't cut anything off the shuttle. As you ponder your predicament, you notice that the shuttle's fuel light has turned on. How will you ever get the shuttle into the space station? (Give up? See page 234.)

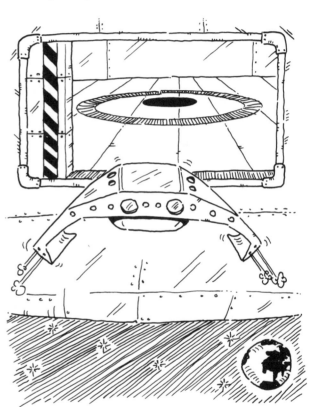

TRAVEL TRIVIA

Among the oldest mountains on Earth, the Great Smokies of North Carolina and Tennessee got their name from the filmy haze produced by their incredible abundance of flowering plants and trees.

JUNGLE MAZE

Professor Stanley is trying to find a safe path to the nest of the Klum-Klum bird. Can you help him?

LOST PLANET MAZE

Help the space traveler find a way back to his spaceship without the alien creature seeing him.

STREET SIGN MAZES

This is a good game for when driving in a city with lots of street signs.

Next time you're driving in a city with lots of one-way streets, use this map to see how quickly you can work your way to the edge. Start in the middle where the map is marked and follow the path your car makes.

Of course, this isn't a map of your city, so you need to use your imagination. Every time your car turns, make one turn on this map and follow the road on the map to the next intersection. Once you get the hang of playing this game with yourself, you might want to make your own street sign map. Or fold a map of where you really are and follow the path your car is driving with your finger! Look out for upcoming street signs.

TRAVEL TRIVIA
Indiana bills itself as the Crossroads of the Nation. The state is within one day's drive of half the population of the United States, and its capital, Indianapolis, is served by more major highways than any other American city.

MAZES & PUZZLES • 141

GOLLY WOLLY

222

It's easy to make your own special riddles. Finding someone who can solve them is another matter!

Golly Wollys are riddles that you make up yourself. Just think of 2 words that rhyme (1 adjective and 1 noun), and you've found the answer. Let's use "big pig" as our example. Next, think of a clue that describes your rhyme. "Large hog" would work. So would "huge sow" or "giant oinker." Say your clue out loud to someone, and see if they can guess what your Golly Wolly is. Can you solve these Golly Wollys? (Answers on page 234.)

- Overweight tabby
- A home for animals that was just built yesterday
- Evening glow
- Fluffy white things that cause thunder
- An automobile that is many miles away
- A stinging insect that doesn't cost anything
- A round toy that is very high

MYSTERY IN INDIA

223

Can you solve your way out of this mystery?

While adventuring in India, you buy a pet tiger, a pet swan, and a huge bag of cashews to share with your family. Walking back to the hotel, you reach a wide, fast river. The bridge is washed out, but you see a tiny boat. An old man nearby says, "You may borrow my boat to cross the river. But because it is small, you can carry only one thing across the river at a time."

Now, you know that tigers hate cashews. But if you leave the tiger and the swan alone together, the tiger will eat the swan. If you leave the swan and the cashews alone together, the swan will eat the cashews. How will you get the tiger, the swan, and the cashews across the river? (Give up? See page 234.)

PIRATE SHIP MAZE

224

Find the shortest route from the deck of the ship to the hidden chest below.

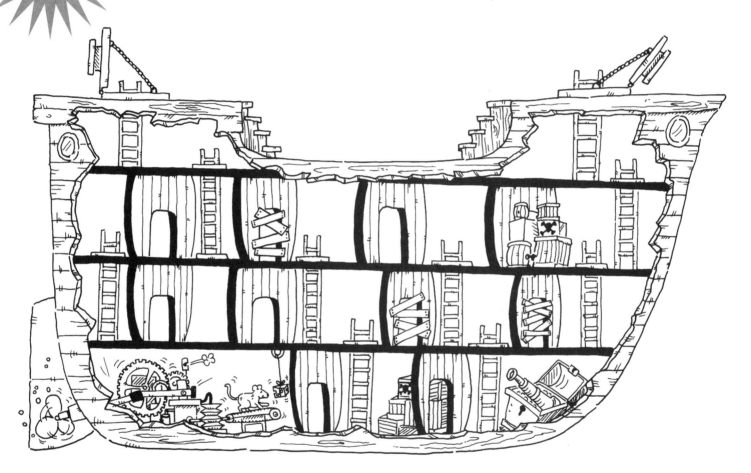

TRAVEL TRIVIA

The largest shipyard in the United States—where ships are built and repaired—is in Newport News, Virginia. Fishing is a major industry in the state, a leader in the harvesting of crabs and oysters.

LINE TRACE #2

225

Here's another picture that was made with one long line. The artist never picked up his pen when drawing it. Follow the line with your finger. Can you find the end of the line?

PERSPECTIVES

Things can really look different when you change your point of view.

Take a look at the objects on the right. Which one matches the shape on the left drawn from a different angle? (Answers on page 234.)

TRUE OR FALSE

You'll need at least 3 players to make this fun game work

You Will Need: Several sheets of notebook or other paper, 3 pens or pencils

Each player gets 1 sheet of paper and 1 pen or pencil. Without talking to each other, each player must think of 10 true-or-false statements to quiz the other 2 players with. Statements can cover subjects currently in the news, things you've learned in school, sports—just about anything, as long as they can be answered with a simple "True" or "False."

Player 1 goes first. He or she begins by reading the first true-or-false statement to Player 2. After Player 2 responds, Player 3 has to agree or disagree with Player 2's answer. If Player 2 was right and Player 3 was wrong, Player 2 gets 10 points. If Player 2 was wrong but Player 3 was right, Player 3 gets 10 points. If both players were right, each gets 5 points.

Player 1's second true-or-false statement goes to Player 3; this time, Player 2 must agree or disagree. Player 1 continues alternating between Players 2 and 3 this way until the quiz is finished. The player with the highest score wins the round.

When Player 1 is finished, it's Player 2's turn to quiz Players 1 and 3 the same way. Then Player 3 quizzes Players 1 and 2. The highest overall score is the winner.

MYSTERY IN SWITZERLAND

228

Can you solve your way out of this mystery?

You and a friend have just finished climbing the highest peaks in the Swiss Alps. You're at the foot of the mountain, waiting for your friend to finish climbing down. Suddenly, 100 feet from the ground, your friend drops his rope! He clings to the face of the rock, terrified. That was a close one! Inch by inch he makes his way to a ledge where he can stand.

"Throw me the rope so I can climb down!" he calls. You try, but the rope is too heavy. You can throw it only halfway up to the ledge before it falls to the ground again. You try to take it to him, but it's too difficult to carry the rope and climb at the same time.

In your backpack you have a canteen full of water, a 500-foot spool of very strong fishing line, a compass, some dirty socks, and your lucky baseball (you never travel without it). How can you get the rope up to your friend before it gets too dark out to see? (Give up? See page 234.)

STATE SWAP

229

Create your own puzzles by combining names of states with other state capitals.

You Will Need: U.S. road atlas

Have you ever been to Albanyork? How about Dallexas? If you haven't, you're not alone. In fact, no one has ever been there—except in their own minds by playing State Swap.

Here's what you do: Think of a city and the state that it is in. Now combine part of the city name with part of the state name to make a brand-new name. In the example above, we combined Albany and New York to get Albanyork. We also combined Dallas and Texas to get Dallexas.

Make a game out of your State Swaps by asking the other players if they've ever been there. For example, "Have you ever been to Orlandorida?" If the other players can guess the State Swap, they say, "Yes, I've been there. It's near Orlando, Florida!" If they can't guess it, they say, "No, I've never been there. Where is it?" You score 1 point for every State Swap they can't guess. The other players score 1 point for every Swap they can guess. Players take turns trading State Swaps. High score wins.

ROAD MAP MYSTERY

Follow each person's path on the map of town, and answer the questions below. (Answers on page 234.)

1. Who visited the post office twice?
2. Who went from the bank to the hospital?
3. Who visited the most places?

4. Who visited the fewest places?
5. Where did Bill go between the hospital and school?

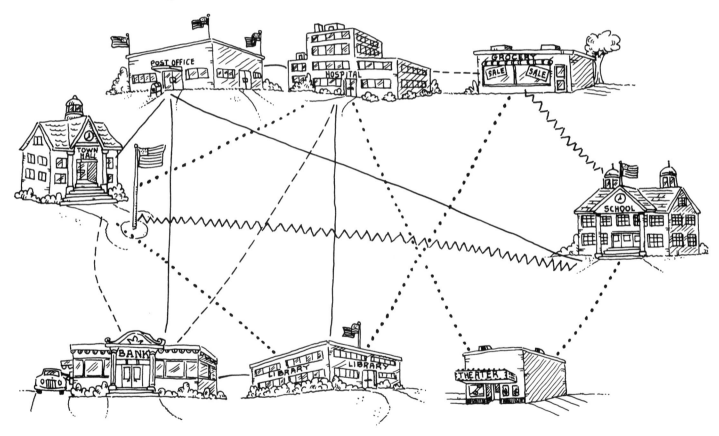

ROAD SIGN SHAPES

The writing from these signs has disappeared—can you tell what each one is just from its shape? (Answers on page 234.)

TRAVEL TRIVIA

Michigan is the only state to border four of the five Great Lakes (Superior, Michigan, Huron, and Erie). The Wolverine State also has the longest coastline of any state except Alaska (3,121 miles).

WHOSE KITE AM I?

See if you can follow the path from each kite to its owner using your finger.

What a windy day! These 4 friends were just in the park, flying their kites, when a huge burst of wind tangled them all up. Can you figure out which kite belongs to which person? (Answers on page 235.)

Ray

Jean

Bill

Lisa

233 ANCIENT EGYPT REBUS

Can you figure out the rebus below? Read the pictures as if they were words.
(Answers on page 235.)

When explorer's found  Tut's , they couldn't

believe their . They found a golden , a giant

made of marble, and made of , and

more and  than they could count.

TRAVEL TRIVIA
The Jefferson National Expansion Memorial—better known as the Gateway Arch—is the tallest monument in the United States. The St. Louis landmark is 630 feet high, besting the District of Columbia's Washington Monument by 75 feet.

HAUNTED HOUSE MAZE

There's only one good way out of a haunted house—as fast as possible!

You're trapped in the attic of a haunted house, and you have to find your way through the house and out through the front door. Watch where you're going. Some rooms and stairs lead to dead ends—or worse!

BOX COUNT

Quick! It's time to take inventory. How many boxes are stacked in this pile?

You might think it's an impossible task, but you really can count what you cannot see if enough clues are provided. In this case, they have been.

Suppose you were working at a warehouse, and your boss told you he has a client on the phone who will buy all of the boxes--provided that there are at least 80 of them. He needs to know right away. Can you figure it out? (Answers on page 235.)

INTERNATIONAL SIGNS

236

These international signs were designed to make travel easier for people who don't speak the same language. Can you guess what each sign means? (Answers on page 235.)

WORD GAMES & TRIVIA

Just about everyone enjoys trivia quizzes. They give us a chance to test our knowledge of popular subjects, while teaching us new things that we weren't aware of. The quizzes in this chapter cover a wide variety of interesting categories, from wildlife and geography to sports and movie monsters. Word games combine fun and learning in a similar way. While youngsters are busy creating secret codes, rhyming and unscrambling words, and taking on tongue twisters, they may not even notice that they are improving their spelling, vocabulary, and use of grammar.

237 WILDLIFE TRIVIA

You may already know that a cat is feline and a dog is canine, but what about these other animals? Match the animal with the word that describes it. (Answers on page 235.)

1. apian
2. avian
3. bovine
4. equine
5. leonine
6. lupine
7. ovine
8. simian
9. taurine
10. ursine

A. bull
B. bear
C. sheep
D. lion
E. ape
F. wolf
G. horse
H. cow
I. bee
J. bird

SPORTS TRIVIA

Test your knowledge of sports. (Answers on page 235.)

1. In baseball, how many players are on the diamond when the other team is at bat?
A. 7
B. 8
C. 9
D. 10

2. The Olympics started more than 100 years ago in 1896. What city hosted the first Games?
A. Athens, Greece
B. Rome, Italy
C. Atlanta, Georgia
D. Paris, France

3. In what country was ice hockey invented?
A. United States
B. Norway
C. Iceland
D. Canada

4. Which of these is NOT a sport in the Summer Olympics?
A. Canoeing
B. Pole vaulting
C. Bowling
D. Badminton

5. The largest fish ever officially caught on a rod weighed 2,664 pounds. That's over 2½ tons—heavier than your car! What kind of fish was it?
A. Blue whale
B. Great white shark
C. Giant tuna
D. Minnow

6. Which of these sports is NOT played with a stick or racket?
A. Lacrosse
B. Jai Alai
C. Croquet
D. Rugby

CROSSED WORDS

You can make your own crossword puzzle for 2 by playing this word-linking game.

You Will Need: Paper, pencil

Mark off a square that contains 15 boxes down and 15 across. Graph paper works best, but if you don't have any, use a ruler to draw the lines on a piece of blank paper. Outline the box in the very center of the puzzle so that it stands out.

Choose a theme for your puzzle, such as flowers, countries, sports, fruits, vegetables, and so on. Player 1 thinks of a word that fits into the chosen category. Then he or she writes the word on the page, 1 letter per box. The first word must have at least 1 letter that goes through the middle box.

Players take turns thinking of words and writing them down. The tricky part is that every word must share a letter with a word that's already on the page. Score 1 point for each letter in a word—but don't count any letters you "borrow" from another word. Play until nobody can think of any more words that will fit on the graph. Highest score wins.

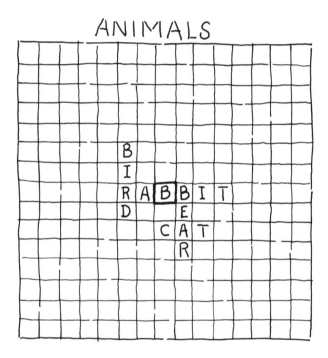

ANIMALS

TRAVEL TRIVIA

The water in Utah's Great Salt Lake is at least four times saltier than the water found in any of the world's oceans.

COUNTING ROUND THE WORLD

240

Learn to count from 1 to 10 in these different languages. Use your new numbers as many times during the day as you can. For example, when you're in an elevator and want to get to the fifth floor, you can say, "Cinq!" which means "five" in French.

GERMAN
eins (eye-ns)
zwei (tsv-eye)
drei (dry)
vier (fear)
funf (foon-f)
sex (zex)
sieben (zee-ben)
acht (oct)
neun (rhymes with coin)
zehn (tsain)

FRENCH
un (uhn)
deux (duh)
trois (twah)
quatre (cat-ruh)
cinq (sank)
six (seize)
sept (set)
huit (wheat)
neuf (nuhf)
dix (rhymes with cease)

JAPANESE
ichi (ee-chee)
ni (nee)
san (sahn)
shi (shee)
go (joh)
roku (row-koo)
shichi (shee-chee)
hachi (ha-chee)
kokonotsu (koko-not-soo)
juu (joo)

GREEK
ena (enna)
dio (thee-oh)
tria (tree-ah)
tessera (tes-sera)
pende (ben-de)
eksi (ek -see)
efta (ef-tuh)
okto (oc-toe)
enea (en-nay-ah)
deka (theka)

BUILDINGS OF THE WORLD

How well do you know your buildings and famous landmarks? (Answers on page 235.)

1. The tallest building in the United States stands 110 stories high. What is its name?
A. World Trade Center, New York City
B. Bank One Tower, Dallas
C. Sears Tower, Chicago
D. Empire State Building, New York City

2. You won't find a hotel anywhere in North America that's bigger than the Excalibur Hotel. It has 4,032 rooms! Where will you find this hotel?
A. Atlantic City, New Jersey
B. Las Vegas, Nevada
C. New York City, New York
D. Los Angeles, California

3. The Superdome, the largest indoor stadium in the world, is 273 feet tall and covers 13 acres. Where can you find the Superdome?
A. Salt Lake City, Utah
B. Orlando, Florida
C. Green Bay, Wisconsin
D. New Orleans, Louisiana

4. The longest road tunnel in the world burrows through more than 10 miles of mountains. That's one big hole! It's called the St. Gotthard Road Tunnel. In what country is it located?
A. Germany
B. Belgium
C. Switzerland
D. Denmark

5. Astronauts say that this is the only human-made object that can be seen from outer space. What is it?
A. The Eiffel Tower in France
B. The Great Wall of China
C. The Great Pyramid in Egypt
D. Buckingham Palace in England

6. The tallest monument in the world is 630 feet tall and 630 feet wide at its base. What is this monument's name, and where will you find it?
A. The Gateway to the West Arch, St. Louis
B. Statue of Liberty, New York City
C. Mount Rushmore, South Dakota
D. Washington Monument, Washington, D.C.

CREATURE QUIZ

If you thought the last quiz was a monster, try this. (Answers on page 235.)

1. In what year was the story *Frankenstein* written?
A. 1985
B. 1710
C. 1818
D. 1936

2. Dr. Jekyll turned into Mr. Hyde the monster after:
A. He drank a potion he had made
B. A witch put an evil curse on him
C. He was struck by lightning
D. He read a book about it

3. Godzilla the dinosaur-monster lived in what country?
A. United States
B. Japan
C. Korea
D. England

4. The Loch Ness monster is said to live in what country?
A. Ireland
B. Scotland
C. Wales
D. England

5. What monster has the body of a lion, the head and wings of an eagle, and the tail of a snake?
A. Griffon
B. Pegasus
C. Centaur
D. Medusa

6. This monster guards the tombs of the ancient Egyptian pharaohs. It has the body of a lion, the face of a human, and the wings of a giant bird. What is its name?
A. Grendel
B. Mothra
C. Sphinx
D. Gorgon

ZOO BABIES

Can you match the animal in Column 1 with its baby name in Column 2? (Answers on page 235.)

COLUMN 1	COLUMN 2
tiger	eaglet
cow	poult
seal	joey
horse	fawn
kangaroo	cygnet
eagle	gosling
goose	kitten
swan	foal
turkey	chick
deer	whelp
rooster	calf

VOLLEYWORD

Volleyball can improve the strength in your arms—but this game can improve your word power!

The basic rule is simple: Players take turns "bouncing" words back and forth as fast as possible without pausing too much between words. Each word must have something to do with the previous player's word.

A word volley might go something like this: dog, cat, nap, bed, sheet, paper, wood, tree, house, and so on. If you don't think that a player has tossed a word that fits with the previous word, challenge it. How long can you keep your word volley going?

ALF-SPEAK

245

ALF is a secret language that's fun to speak with a friend—and nobody else will know what you're saying!

Learning Alf-Speak is easy. Just follow these steps:

Add the letters "lf" after every vowel sound in a word. Then repeat the vowel sound and finish the word. For example, the word "hot" in Alf-Speak is "holfot." Cow is "colfow." Jumbo is "julfumbolfo." Here's a short list of words to get you started.

up - **ulfup**
down - **dowlfown**
you - **youlfou**
me - **melfe**
house - **houlfouse**

ice cream - **ilfice crealfeam**
pumpkin - **pulfumpkilfin**
snowman - **snolfowmalfan**
car - **calfar**
alfalfa - **alfalfalfalfalfa**

Look at this sentence written in Alf-Speak. Can you translate it?

Thelfe lilfittle bolfoy ralfan tolfo thelfe stolfore.

May I please have an Ilfice Crealfeam?

DICTIONARY

The object of the game is to figure out the word by listening to its definition.

You Will Need: Pocket dictionary

First, let all the players know how many pages are in the dictionary you will be using. The reader holds the dictionary and says, "Which page?" Someone else calls out a page number. The reader then turns to that page and asks, "Which column?" (Smaller dictionaries may have 1 column on a page instead of 2. If your dictionary has just 1 column, skip this step.) Someone calls out left or right.

Finally, the reader asks, "How many?" Someone calls out a number from 1 to 10. From the top of the page, the reader counts down that many words and reads the definition out loud. Everyone else tries to guess what the word is. If no one can guess, you may give clues. For example, you could tell them the first letter of the word, or you could read the definition of the word above or below the chosen word. The player who guess correctly becomes the reader. If no one guesses, start the game again with a new word.

YOUR NEW NAME

If you could pick another name for yourself, what would it be?

In some parts of the world, people have more than just a first name, a middle name, and a last name. They are also given special names that tell something about their families or their personalities. Create your own special name based on the name you already have. To do this, take the first letter of your first name. Then think of a word beginning with that letter that tells something about you or your interests.

For example, if a person named James Smith loved to jump rope, the word "jumping" might do the trick. From now on, you could be called "Jumping Jim" Smith. If you want, you can continue by using each letter in your name to start a new word that describes you. Then combine them all into one list. James's new name is "Jumping Athletic Mysterious Extra-Silly James" Smith!

CAT QUIZ

Here's a trivia quiz that's purr-fect for cat lovers. (Answers on page 235.)

1. What cat is the fastest animal in the world, running up to 70 miles per hour?
A. Cheetah
B. Tomcat
C. Bengal tiger
D. Black panther

2. Which two members of the cat family don't climb?
A. Lion and cheetah
B. Tiger and cheetah
C. Lion and tiger
D. Panther and lion

3. Which part of a cat is stronger than any other animals'?
A. Tooth
B. Tail
C. Rib
D. Claw

4. Which of the following is NOT a member of the cat family?
A. Lion
B. Polecat
C. Tiger
D. Siamese

5. The Cheshire Cat could slowly disappear, leaving only its smile behind. In what book can you read about this magical cat?
A. *Cat's Cradle*
B. *Harriet the Spy*
C. *Witches' Brew*
D. *Alice In Wonderland*

6. What famous words does cartoon character Sylvester the Cat always say?
A. "Exit, stage left!"
B. "To the rescue!"
C. "Sufferin' succotash!"
D. "Cowabunga, dude!"

LADYBUG

Guess the other player's secret word before the ladybug flies away.

Player 1 thinks of a secret word. Then he or she counts up the letters in the word and draws that many lines next to each other on a piece of paper. Player 2 tries to guess what the secret word is, 1 letter at a time. If Player 2 guesses a letter correctly, Player 1 writes the letter in its proper place on the lines. But if Player 2 guesses a letter that is not in the word, then Player 1 draws on a new part of the ladybug. (The bug has 8 parts in all.)

Player 2 must guess the secret word before the ladybug is finished or else the ladybug flies away—and Player 2 loses the round.

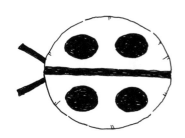

RHYME TIME #2

In the paragraphs below, replace each word in capital letters with a word that rhymes with it so that the story makes sense. We have done the first one for you. (Answers on page 235.)

Once upon a DIME (time), there was a young CURL by the GAME of Goldilocks—but her BENDS called her MOLDY. One PAY while MOLDY was MOCKING through the forest, a DIG, hairy brown CHAIR jumped out from behind a KNEE and said, "Didn't I BATCH you in my MOUSE last GEAR?"

"No!" said MOLDY. "I've never GREEN you before in my whole KNIFE!"

"I STINK you're CRYING," said the CHAIR. "You TAME into my MOUSE and ate all my LOOP! Then you broke my favorite HAIR! Then you went to DEEP in my RED! I'd GROW you anywhere!"

So MOLDY TAN away as PASSED as she could and didn't COOK SACK once.

WACKY WORDS

251

Have you ever heard someone try to finish a joke or a story—but fail because he or she couldn't think of the right word?

If you have, you might enjoy making up wacky word stories for other people. All you need to do is write your own story and leave out some of the words. Make a note of what kind of word or part of speech the missing word is. Then ask your friends to "fill in the blanks" before they hear the story.

Below are the first few sentences of a wacky word story. Before you read it aloud, go through it and ask the other players to give you a word that fits each requirement (in parentheses). In the sample below, you would say, "Give me a boy's name." Write down the word you are given. Next you would say, "Give me an adjective." Write down the word. Do the same thing for the rest of the story. When you have all the words you need, read the story out loud, putting in the words you were given into the right places. You won't believe some of the wacky stories you'll get!

Once there was a Prince named (boy's name) who was very (adjective). The Prince loved to play practical jokes. Who can forget the time he surprised Queen (woman's name) with a big, fat (noun) that he hid in her (noun)? We all (verb ending in "-ed") for days!

TRAVEL TRIVIA

Visitors to Tennessee can ride the world's steepest incline-railway at Chattanooga's Lookout Mountain. On a clear day, you can see five different states from the top.

DOG QUIZ

How much do you know about "man's best friend"? (Answers on page 235.)

1. Which of the following is a dog's sharpest sense?

A. Smell
B. Sight
C. Touch
D. Taste

2. What is the heaviest dog, weighing in at a record 305 pounds?

A. Saint Bernard
B. Bullmastiff
C. Rottweiler
D. Great Dane

3. How many teeth does a dog have?

A. 36
B. 58
C. 42
D. 28

4. What is the world's fastest dog?

A. Irish setter
B. Whippet
C. Cocker Spaniel
D. Greyhound

5. What kind of dog doesn't bark?

A. Pekinese
B. Dachshund
C. Basenji
D. Akita

6. What is the smallest breed of dog in the world?

A. Schnauzer
B. Poodle
C. West Highland terrier
D. Chihuahua

TAG-TEAM WORDS

Outsmart the other players and be the first person to finish a word.

Players take turns saying one letter at a time. The winner is the first player to add a letter that completes a real word. Let's play a sample game with 2 players:

Player 1 says the letter S. Player 2 adds the letter T. Player 1 adds the letter U, even though she knows that if Player 2 says the letter B, he'll win the game, because STUB is a word. Lucky for Player 1, Player 2 doesn't think of the letter B. Instead, he adds the letter M. Player 1 thinks for a moment, and then adds the letter P. This makes the word STUMP, so she wins the round!

If a player tries to add a letter than cannot make a real word—adding a Q after a T, for example—the other person can say, "I challenge you!" If the challenged person cannot make a real word using those letters, the challenger wins the round. But if the challenged person does think of a word, then he or she wins.

FAMILY TRIVIA

How well do you know your house and your family?

Before you begin, each player makes up 3 or 4 trivia questions about your house and family. (We started you out with some questions below.) Be as original as you can—just make sure you know the right answer!

Write each question on a small piece of paper and fold the paper in half. Then everyone takes a turn reading the questions aloud and letting the others answer. Whoever answers the most questions correctly wins.

~ How many windows are in our house?
~ How many drawers are in the kitchen?
~ How many brothers and sisters does grandma have?
~ What color is the shower curtain?
~ Whose picture is hanging in the dining room?
~ How many steps are there leading to the basement?

CREATE-A-CODE

255

Make your own code and send secret messages to your friends.

Try this code the next time you want to send a secret message to your friend. Write out the message you want to send on a scrap piece of paper (Picture 1). Pick a special code letter that only you and your friend know. We'll use the letter R. Add that letter to the end of every word in your message.

Now write out the letters on a clean sheet of paper. Divide the letters into groups of 2 and write them out (Picture 2). Now send it to your friend. To solve it, your friend must write the letters out in one long word. Then he or she crosses out your code letter. Make sure your friend does not cross out a code letter that is a part of your secret message.

To make this code even harder for other people to crack, you can write out the message backward before you add your code letter. Now that's a tough code!

Picture 1   **Picture 2**

VACATION SCRAMBLE

256

Hurry! Can you unscramble these vacation words before your trip is over? (Answers on page 235.)

RUFS	ROFSET	EPALN	CHEAB
NADS	NETT	CIKETT	MINGWIMS
NOECA	PINCIC	SUMMUE	FRAMPICE
OLOP	SAMP	ROUT	LOHTE
ARC	REVID	CURKT	DIHAYOL

WORD SPLURGE

Have you ever looked through a dictionary to see how many words begin with the same letter? If you have, you're a natural-born word splurger!

To test your word-splurging abilities, have someone pick a letter of the alphabet and then say "Go." As that person watches the clock (60 seconds is a good length of time), write down as many words as you can think of that begin with that letter.

At the end of 60 seconds, count up your words. (They must be real words that you can find in a dictionary.) If there is another word splurger in the group, have a race to see who can think of the most words. Keep track of how fast you are with different letters. The next time you play, try to beat your old scores.

BONDED

The object of this game is to bond together a word, forward and backward.

Pick a word. Short words make a shorter game; long words make a longer game. Make 3 vertical columns. Write the word down the left column, one letter atop the other. Next, write the same word backward (last letter first) down the right column. Now try to "bond" the columns of letters together by adding whatever letters you can think of in the middle column to spell words across. We did 2 sample games below using the word "horse." Players score 1 point for each letter in the middle column, so the longer the word, the more points you get.

H	om	E = 2		H	umbl	E = 4
O	ur	S = 2		O	ctopu	S = 5
R	oa	R = 2		R	ive	R = 3
S		O = 0		S	tere	O = 4
E	art	H = 3		E	nglis	H = 5

Points = 9   Points = 21

DECONSTRUCTION

259

You usually get in trouble for taking something apart. But not in this game!

"Construction" is a word you might see on a building or along a highway. It means that something is being built. But this word game is about deconstruction—taking things apart.

The object of the game is to make as many smaller words out of another word as possible. For example, consider all of the words you can create using the word TRAVELING: travel, grave, gave, give, tin, get, gravel, rain, grain, veil, vane, great, lean, near, ring, tale, liar, tear, gear.

Pick a nice, long word, and see how many new words you can make from it. Letters may be used only once in each new word—unless there's more than one of the same letter in the original (such as the letter D in the word MIDDLE). If you play with another person, the winner is the one who thinks up the most words.

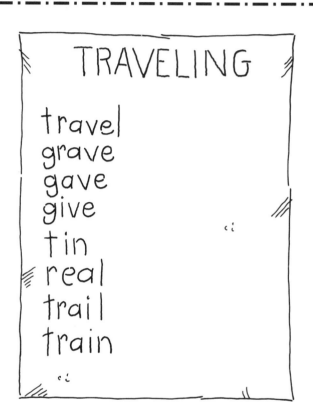

TRAVELING

travel
grave
gave
give
tin
real
trail
train

TOSSED WORDS

260

How big of a word salad can you toss?

Start by picking a category of words you want to toss around—for example, names, animals, or foods. Player 1 picks a word from that category and says it aloud. The next player takes the last letter of that word and "tosses" a new word back that starts with that letter. For example, a name toss might go like this: Nancy…Yolanda…Adam…Michael…Lawrence…and so on.

INVENTORS QUIZ

How well do you know your inventors? (Answers on page 235.)

1. What did George Eastman invent in 1888?
A. Motorcycle
B. Test tube
C. Ice cream
D. Camera

2. What did Gail Borden invent in 1853?
A. Condensed milk
B. Cottage cheese
C. Yarn
D. Fluoride toothpaste

3. What did Clarence Birdseye invent in 1924?
A. Electricity
B. Wool underwear
C. Frozen food
D. Remote control

4. What did Charles Goodyear invent in 1839?
A. The blimp
B. A way to make rubber
C. Internal-combustion engine
D. Porcelain toilets

5. What did W. L. Judson invent in 1891?
A. Zipper
B. Shoelace
C. Pacifier
D. Freezer bags

6. What did Alfred Nobel invent in 1867?
A. Dynamite
B. Magnifying glass
C. Electric train
D. Skateboard

TRAVEL TRIVIA

Where would you use these things to travel? (Answers on page 235.)

1. Gondola	A. Dominican Republic
2. Sleigh	B. England
3. Kayak	C. Italy
4. Rickshaw	D. France
5. Sampan	E. Alaska
6. Lorry	F. Peru
7. Motovelo	G. Japan
8. Zeppelin	H. China
9. Motoconcho	I. Norway
10. Alpaca	J. Germany

CITY NICKNAMES

263

Match the real names of these 10 cities to their nicknames. (Answers on page 235.)

1 Chicago	A. Big Apple
2. Los Angeles	B. Bean Town
3. Minneapolis/St. Paul	C. City of Light
4. Indianapolis	D. Bride of the Sea
5. New York City	E. City of Angels
6. Boston	F. The Eternal City
7. Paris	G. Windy City
8. Philadelphia	H. Crossroads of America
9. Rome	I. Twin Cities
10. Venice	J. City of Brotherly Love

WORD RECYCLE

264

There are so many things you can recycle: aluminum cans, plastic bottles, egg cartons—and words. Words, you ask? Read on!

The object is to recycle a word into a completely different word by changing one letter at a time. Every time you change a letter, the new word must be a real word. To play, think of 2 words that have the same number of letters and write them down. The players try to recycle the first word into the second word. If more than 1 person is playing, the player who recycles the words using the least amount of steps in-between is the winner. Here are 2 examples to get you started.

Recycle a CAR into a BUS:

CAR
BAR
BAT
BUT
BUS

Recycle a COAT into a VEST:

COAT
COST
CAST
VAST
VEST

TRANSFORMATION

This game is similar to Word Recycle, but this time you're recycling a whole sentence.

The object of this game is to change a sentence into a completely different sentence by changing one word at a time. Start by writing down a simple sentence (10 words or less). Players take turns changing one word in the sentence until all the words have been changed.

Replace each word with a word that's the same part of speech. The sentence must still make sense when you replace a word, even though it might sound silly. For example, in the sentence, "The boy ran to the store," you could change "boy" to "goat" but you couldn't change "boy" to "running." When the sentence has been completely transformed, start another. Here's a sample to get you started:

The tall girl bounced the ball.
The tall cow bounced the ball.
The fat cow bounced the ball.
The fat cow ate the ball.
The fat cow ate the hay.
A fat cow ate the hay.
A fat cow ate some hay.

TONGUE TWISTERS

How fast can you correctly say these terribly twisted tongue twisters? Move too fast, and you may have to un-tongue your tangle!

1. Rubber baby-buggy bumper. (Repeat 5 times)
2. Three tall tree tops. (Repeat 5 times)
3. How much wood would a woodchuck chuck if a woodchuck could chuck wood?
4. He shells and she sells seashells by the shady seashore.
5. Charlie Shu chooses Sherry Chu's shoes to chew.

HOLIDAY TRIVIA

Test your knowledge of American holidays. (Answers on page 235.)

1. This holiday was first celebrated in New York City in 1882 on the first Monday in September.
A. Memorial Day
B. Groundhog Day
C. Secretaries Day
D. Labor Day

2. This holiday celebrates the adoption of the Continental Congress on June 14, 1777.
A. Independence Day
B. Pearl Harbor Day
C. Flag Day
D. Veterans Day

3. This fourth Thursday in November was made into a national holiday more than 130 years ago in 1863.
A. Palm Sunday
B. Thanksgiving
C. Father's Day
D. All Saints Day

4. This holiday was started in 1907 and falls on the second Sunday in May.
A. Summer Solstice
B. Halloween
C. Mother's Day
D. Grandparents Day

5. This holiday was first celebrated in 1910 and falls on the third Sunday in June.
A. Mardi Gras
B. Good Friday
C. Father's Day
D. Election Day

6. What month of the year is named after Julius Caesar, a famous Roman emperor?
A. June
B. March
C. August
D. July

PLAYBACK

268

Pretend that 1 player is a Sentence-Making Machine, and the other player is a scientist feeding information into it.

The scientist writes down a list of words. You decide how many, but it's best to start with just 4 or 5 until you get the hang of the game. The scientist then reads them aloud to the other player (the Sentence-Making Machine). The important thing is to read slowly—but read the list only once.

The Sentence-Making Machine then shows how well it works by using all of those words in 1 sentence, if it can, while the scientist keeps track of how many words the Machine remembered, giving 1 point for each. Here's an example. The scientist says, "Boat, water, fish, wave, jump." The Sentence-Making Machine says, "The fish jumped out of the water and into the boat." That scores 4 points. The Machine didn't use the word "wave" so it doesn't get any points for it.

Now switch roles! Try to give each other the same number of words each time. Does your score improve the more often you play?

WORD JIVE

269

You should always tell the truth—except when you're playing Word Jive!

You Will Need: A dictionary, pens or pencils

The object of this game is to invent definitions for a word and trick people into choosing the wrong definition. Player 1 picks a word out of the dictionary and writes down the definition on a piece of paper. Then Player 2 does the same thing, and so on, depending on how many players you have. Players then make up 2 false definitions for the word they chose. Try to make the false definition "fit" the word. For example, the real definition of the word COROLLA is "the petals of a flower." False definitions might be "the metal ring that holds an eraser on a pencil," or "a type of crayon used long ago."

When players are finished writing their false definitions, each player reads aloud his or her definitions one by one. The other players write down which definition they think is the correct one without talking it over with anyone. The first player then says which definition is correct. Whoever guesses correctly wins 1 point. If no one guesses correctly, the player who made up the definition gets 1 point. The first player to reach 10 points wins.

HOMONYM HUNT

Quick, grab your net! Homonyms are on the loose!

270

Homonyms are words that sound alike but have different meanings. When they get loose, they have a habit of working their way into sentences where they don't belong. Hunt down the right homonym in the following sentences. (Answers on page 235.)

1. Where is *there/their* mother?
2. Do you think *its/it's* cold outside?
3. She needs a new *pear/pair* of shoes for school.
4. The wind *blue/blew* the tree down last night.
5. Take a walk down *to/too/two* the store.
6. The girl *through/threw* the ball in the air.
7. When the audience claps, take a *bow/bough*.
8. The *rein/rain/reign* came pouring down.
9. Use a *plain/plane* to shave wood off a board.
10. I won't *boar/bore* you with the details.

Make your own Homonym Hunt by thinking of a homonym and using it in a sentence. It's up to the other player to "capture" the homonym by saying it aloud and spelling it properly.

TRAVEL TRIVIA

New Jersey is one of the five smallest states, yet it has more people per square mile than any other state in the Union.

OUTER SPACE TRIVIA

Here's a trivia quiz that's out of this world. (Answers on page 235.)

1. On April 12, 1961, who became the first human being in outer space?
A. Alan Shepherd
B. John Glenn
C. Gordon Cooper
D. Yuri Gagarin

2. Who was the first person to walk on the moon in July of 1969?
A. Neil Armstrong
B. Edwin Aldrin
C. Michael Collins
D. Buck Rogers

3. What was the name of the first space shuttle, launched on April 12, 1981?
A. Enterprise
B. Queen Mary
C. Columbia
D. Titanic

4. What is the largest planet in the solar system?
A. Earth
B. Pluto
C. Venus
D. Jupiter

5. What planet is closest to the sun?
A. Venus
B. Mars
C. Mercury
D. Neptune

6. What is the red spot that is visible on the planet Jupiter when you look at it through a telescope?
A. Meteorite crater
B. Storm
C. Lake
D. Volcano

SPELLING BEE

272

Who's the best speller in your group? There is only one way to find out—with a spelling contest!

You Will Need: A dictionary

You've probably been in more than your fair share of spelling bees in school. But having a spelling bee with your family and friends is a lot more fun. All you need is a dictionary. Take turns giving each other words to spell. As soon as someone misses, it's that person's turn to give a word to someone else. See who can spell the most words correctly in a row.

Make any special group rules before you begin. For example, you could decide on a letter limit—no more than 6 letters in a word. Another good ground rule is that players have to give each other words that they've thought of before looking in the dictionary. That way you won't be trying to spell words that are too weird or wacky.

SENTENCE SPROUTS

273

Did you know that sentences are one of the fastest growing things on this planet? You'll see why when you play this game.

You Will Need: Paper, pencils

Start with someone saying a short phrase that everybody knows. Phrases such as "with liberty and justice for all" or "once upon a time" work well. Each player writes down that phrase, then adds another couple of lines—whatever he or she can think of. When everyone is done, share your sentences with one another. All of the sentences will probably sound very different, but they all sprouted from the same seed of a phrase.

STATE TRIVIA

274

Match the following states with their nickname. (Answers on page 235.)

1. Old Line State
2. Palmetto State
3. Granite State
4. Hoosier State
5. Magnolia State
6. Land of Opportunity
7. Golden State
8. Sagebrush State
9. Peace Garden State
10. Beehive State

A. Mississippi
B. Indiana
C. Arkansas
D. California
E. Maryland
F. South Carolina
G. North Dakota
H. Nevada
I. Utah
J. New Hampshire

RHYME OR REASON #1

275

Replace each word in capital letters with a word that rhymes with it so that the story makes sense. The first one has been done for you. (Answers on page 236.)

Tommy plays a SCUBA (tuba) in the TOOL HAND. He loves to GLIDE his FOUNTAIN MIKE and play ROCKER with his friends. His favorite RUDE is macaroni and SNEEZE with a big helping of WRENCH PIES. In the WARNING he delivers CAPERS and saves all his HONEY for a trip to BLUE FORK city to see the CURLED BRAID Center. When he MOWS up, he wants to be a TIRE BITER.

GUESS THE TITLE

276

We took 10 book, song, and movie titles—and a couple of nursery rhymes—and rephrased them using different words. Can you match up the 2 lists below? (Answers on page 236.)

1. Pale girl and a bunch of little men
2. Prehistoric habitat
3. Feline with headgear
4. Strange breakfast food
5. Magician in the Emerald City
6. Congratulations on your anniversary
7. A giant egg perched on a fence
8. The girl had a small woolly pet
9. Twinkling lights in the sky during battle
10. I toiled on the tracks

A. Mary had a little lamb
B. I've been working on the railroad
C. The Cat in the Hat
D. Star Wars
E. Snow White and the Seven Dwarfs
F. Jurassic Park
G. Green Eggs and Ham
H. The Wizard of Oz
I. Humpty Dumpty sat on a wall
J. Happy Birthday

ANIMAL TRIVIA

See how much you know about animals with this trivia test. (Answers on page 236.)

1. This bird has the longest migration pattern among all birds. Averaging almost 100 miles a day, it covers around 22,000 miles each year.
A. seagull
B. bald eagle
C. arctic tern
D. swallow

2. Octopuses and squid have eyes most similar to which land animal:
A. humans
B. deer
C. elephant
D. turtles

3. A German Shepherd's nose has an average of 220 million nose smells, making its sense of smell how much more sensitive than a human being's?
A. 100 times
B. 1,000 times
C. 100,000 times
D. 1,000,000 times

4. Which of the following critters can jump so high that it is the same as a human being jumping to the roof of a 70-story building?
A. cricket
B. flea
C. dragonfly
D. beetle

5. The peregrine falcon is the world's fastest moving animal. How fast does it dive for its dinner?
A. 100 mph
B. 128 mph
C. 173 mph
D. over 200 mph

6. The baby blue whale is one of the fastest growing mammals, gaining up to 200 pounds per day. How much milk do you think a baby whale drinks to keep growing that fast?
A. up to 50 gallons per day
B. 50–100 gallons per day
C. 100–150 gallons per day
D. more than 150 gallons per day

MORSE CODE

278

Once you know the code, you can make words out of dots and dashes.

Back in 1838, Samuel Morse created a special code that was named after him. In his code, a dot is a short tap and a dash is a long tap (with more time in between taps, that is). People used his code to send messages before telephones or radios were invented.

Morse designed his code so that the most often used letters in the alphabet have the shortest signals. Tap out your own messages in Morse Code on your knee. A short tap for the dots, a longer tap for the dashes. Have your friend write out your message and read it back to you. Take turns.

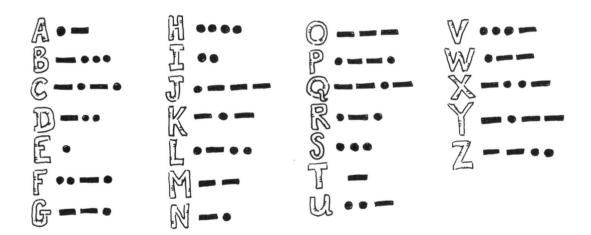

TRAVEL TRIVIA

Iowa may be the quintessential farm state. Typically, it ranks first in corn and pigs, third in cattle production. Some 90 percent of the state is used for farming.

TURNING PHRASES

279

Sometimes old sayings are hard to figure out because they don't sound like what they mean. Can you match up the sayings below with what they really mean? (Answers on page 236.)

1. Grab the bull by the horns.
2. That's par for the course.
3. A bird in the hand is worth two in the bush.
4. He really gets my goat.
5. Hold your horses.
6. I smell a rat.
7. Never cry wolf.
8. There's a wolf in sheep's clothing.
9. You'll catch more flies with honey than with vinegar.
10. That's water under the bridge.

A. He's pretending to be something he's not.
B. Someone is telling a lie.
C. You'll make more friends if you're nice.
D. It always happens that way.
E. Don't worry about things that have already happened.
F. Get right to work on a problem.
G. What you have is more valuable than what you don't.
H. Don't lie, especially about important things.
I. Wait a minute.
J. He irritates me.

DON'T SAY IT

280

What you don't say matters more than what you do say!

Players take turns asking one another any type of question, followed by a letter from the alphabet. The next person has to answer that question without using the letter provided.

For example, one player might ask, "What's your favorite food? You can't use the letter S." The other person had better not answer soup! Pizza would be a great answer, though, because it doesn't have the letter S in it.

This game can get pretty tricky depending on the type of questions you decide to ask. If you really want to make it more fun, give 2 or 3 letters that can't be used after you ask a question. For example, "What's another way of saying 'President of the United States'? You can't use the letter M, I, or L." One answer might be, "The head of the country."

UNCLE ELMER

281

Just about everyone has someone in their family who is a little different, but Uncle Elmer is special.

Uncle Elmer is a strange old guy. He only likes certain things. For example, he like apples, but he doesn't like oranges. He likes ladders, but he doesn't like steps. He likes butter, but he doesn't like margarine. Can you guess why? Because Uncle Elmer only likes words with double letters!

To play Uncle Elmer, one player silently decides what really makes Uncle Elmer unusual. Perhaps he only likes words with the letter E in them, or objects that are red, or have wheels, or make noises. Then this player gives clues about Uncle Elmer's likes and dislikes to the other players, who try to figure out the special rule. When someone catches on and gives a few examples that fit the rule, that person gets a turn talking about Uncle Elmer.

BACKWARD BEE

282

There are 2 fun ways to have a backward spelling bee.

Method 1: Just like in a regular spelling bee, you take turns giving each other words to spell. However, when it is your turn to spell, you have to spell it backward. No fair writing it down first! Keep score to see who is the best backward speller (1 point for each correct word).

Method 2: Instead of you spelling the word backward, someone else spells a word for you backward. The first person to figure out what the word is scores 1 point.

GEOGRAPHY QUIZ

283

Test yourself to see how much you know about the world around you. (Answers on page 236.)

1. At 20,320 feet, this is the highest mountain in the United States.
A. Mount St. Helens
B. Mount Rainier
C. Mount McKinley
D. Pike's Peak

2. At 4,180 miles, this is the longest river in the world.
A. Nile River
B. Tigris River
C. Mississippi River
D. Amazon River

3. At 29,028 feet, this is the highest mountain in the world.
A. Mount Rushmore
B. Mount Everest
C. Kilimanjaro
D. Mount Washington

4. At 3,212 feet, this is the highest waterfall on earth.
A. Angel Falls, Venezuela
B. Niagara Falls, New York
C. Clifty Falls, Indiana
D. Bushkill Falls, Pennsylvania

5. At 3,212 square miles, this is the world's largest freshwater lake.
A. Lake Superior
B. Lake Okeechobee
C. Lake Michigan
D. Lake Huron

6. Mammoth Caves National Park—the largest cave system in the world, with more than 300 miles of tunnels—stays at what temperature year-round?
A. 85 degrees
B. 69 degrees
C. 54 degrees
D. 30 degrees

WHICH IS WHICH?

284

Some animals look alike but are actually very different. Do you know which is which? (Answers on page 236.)

1. What do you call a 1-hump camel—a dromedary or a Bactrian?
2. Which has a long, tapered snout—a crocodile or an alligator?
3. Which has long, floppy ears—an Asian elephant or an African elephant?
4. Which has moist, smooth skin—a frog or a toad?
5. Which insect has 8 legs—a spider or a beetle?
6. Which live on land all the time—tortoises or turtles?
7. What's the difference between a panther, a puma, a cougar, and a mountain lion?
8. Which has 1 horn—the Indian rhinoceros or the African rhinoceros?
9. Which has a white stripe down its back—the American skunk or the European skunk?
10. Which monkeys can hang by their tails—African monkeys or South American monkeys?

STORE STORY

285

Walk through the store backward—and don't forget your shopping list!

Player 1 starts the game by saying, "I went to the store and bought _____." Fill in the blank with a word that begins with the letter Z. The next player repeats the sentence and adds a word that begins with the letter Y, then X, and so on, backward through the alphabet until someone forgets a word or you reach the letter A.

WHEN DID THAT HAPPEN?

286

Can you match the invention or discovery below with the correct year in which it happened? (Answers on page 236.)

1.	1509	A.	Air Pump
2.	1592	B.	Telegraph
3.	1650	C.	Motion Pictures
4.	1712	D.	The Planet Pluto Discovered
5.	1783	E.	Hot Air Balloon
6.	1786	F.	Telephone
7.	1832	G.	Thermometer
8.	1876	H.	Electrical Battery
9.	1889	I.	Pocketwatch
10.	1930	J.	Steam Engine

BUILDING BLOCKS

287

You have heard of building with blocks, bricks, and wood—but have you ever built anything out of letters?

Below are 7 consonants that are waiting to become words. See how many words you can create using any 2 or 3 of them, plus the letter A. We found 18. (Answers on page 236.)

B N G P L D M

When you finish this puzzle, try making your own building block games by using different consonants. Just remember to use only 1 vowel, and never use the same letter twice in 1 word.

FOOD TRIVIA

288

Try this trivia quiz when you start getting hungry. (Answers on page 236.)

1. About half of the world's population depends on this crop for its daily food supply:
A. rice
B. wheat
C. beans
D. milk

2. All potatoes—white, sweet, and yams—originally came from:
A. South and Central America
B. Africa
C. Europe
D. New Zealand

3. This food was called a "love apple" when it was first introduced in Europe in the 1500s:
A. tomato
B. potato
C. plum
D. strawberry

4. Peaches originally came from:
A. China
B. Persia
C. South America
D. Georgia

5. This natural sweetener was used by ancient Egyptians as early as 4000 B.C.
A. honey
B. syrup
C. molasses
D. sugar

6. The first hamburger chain in America opened in 1921 and was called:
A. White Castle
B. McDonalds
C. Burger Boy
D. Hamburger Heaven

289

BACK MESSAGE

This game will have people "talking behind your back"!

Do you know the story of Helen Keller? She was born blind and deaf, but she learned to communicate when her teacher spelled words into her hand.

Close your eyes and have a partner gently spell out a word on your back, one letter at a time, using his or her finger. Can you figure out what the person is writing? It helps to draw the letters slowly at first. You can also try spelling out messages on the palms of your hands, like Helen Keller used to do.

AN APPLE A DAY

290

Some doctors treat only kids. They're called pediatricians. Other doctors treat only animals. They're called veterinarians. Can you match the name of the doctor below with the kind of doctoring they do? (Answers on page 236.)

1. Anesthesiologist
2. Cardiologist
3. Dermatologist
4. Gerontologist
5. Hematologist
6. Nephrologist
7. Obstetrician
8. Orthodontist
9. Otolaryngologist
10. Radiologist

A. Treats old people
B. Treats kidney problems
C. Treats pregnant women
D. Straightens people's teeth
E. Treats the ear, nose, and throat
F. Makes X rays
G. Treats the skin
H. Puts patients to sleep before surgery
I. Treats blood problems
J. Treats heart problems

FAMOUS NAME CHANGES

291

Have you ever thought about changing your name? Many people in Hollywood changed the names they were born with to "stage names" that sound more like famous people. See if you can match the stars with their real names. (Answers on page 236.)

HOLLYWOOD STAR
1. Alan Alda
2. Woody Allen
3. Fred Astaire
4. Cher
5. John Denver
6. Judy Garland
7. Cary Grant
8. Marilyn Monroe
9. John Wayne
10. Stevie Wonder

BORN AS
A. Frederick Austerlitz
B. Norma Jean Baker
C. Steveland Judkins Morris
D. Archibald Leach
E. Marion Morrison
F. Allen Steward Konigsberg
G. Alphonso D'Abruzzo
H. Frances Gumm
I. Henry John Deutschendorf, Jr.
J. Cherilyn Sarkisian

RHYME OR REASON #2

292

In the paragraph below, replace each word in capital letters with a word that rhymes with it so the story makes sense. (Answers on page 236.)

Julius Johnson owns a small CHORE on Maple BEAT. He sells plates, FISHES, and cups, as well as WIVES, forks and GOONS. His grandBOTHER started the family business in a TON-room building LACK in 1929. Now Julius BELLS lots of useful DINGS to eat with from all around the CURLED. Last week, he COLD five hundred ROLLS made out of BLUBBER that won't break if you HOP them on the floor. What will he STINK of next?

HUMAN BODY TRIVIA

How much do you know about your own body? (Answers on page 236.)

1. How many cells are there in a newborn baby?
A. 26 million
B. 1 million
C. 5,000
D. 10

2. How long does it take food to travel 30 feet through the human body?
A. 10 minutes
B. 4 hours
C. 24 hours
D. 1 week

3. What is the strongest muscle?
A. Leg muscle
B. Arm muscle
C. Finger muscle
D. Jaw muscle

4. How many different tastes can the human tongue sense?
A. 4
B. 8
C. 20
D. 10,000

5. How long does it take a fingernail to grow from its base to the tip?
A. 1 week
B. 6 months
C. 1 year
D. 5 years

6. How much of the human body is made of water?
A. 10 percent
B. 43 percent
C. 65 percent
D. 90 percent

TRAVEL TRIVIA

Connecticut's name comes from the Pequot Indian term meaning "long river." The Connecticut River, running north to south through the center of the state, is the longest river in New England.

ODDS & ENDS

This is the chapter where you'll find all kinds of games and activities that, for one reason or another, don't quite fit under the other chapter headings. The list includes card games, sing-alongs, connect-the-dot games, magic tricks, numbers games, sound effects games, and a few that don't seem to fit any general category at all. Whether you want to make a hot dog float between your fingers, learn how to thumb wrestle, conduct an orchestra, or describe what kind of pet you might have had if you had lived 1,000 years ago, there's plenty here to keep everyone amused.

FINGER SAUSAGE

294

Did you know that you have a secret power? It's true! You can make a hot dog float between your fingers!

Okay, it's not a real hot dog, but it sure looks like one. Here's how to do it: Hold your hands up about 6 inches in front of your eyes with the tips of your index (pointer) fingers touching. Now slowly pull your fingers apart about 1 inch. To see the floating hot dog, don't look at your fingers—look at something in front of you, such as the car seat.

As soon as you look beyond your fingers, an image that looks like a hot dog will appear floating in the air! Move your fingers closer together or farther apart to make the hot dog bigger or smaller. To make it disappear, just look at your fingers again!

SOUND EFFECTS

295

A picture is worth a thousand words—and so is a sound!

You Will Need: A tape recorder

Sounds are all around you: loud ones, soft ones. Sounds that repeat and sounds that you have to wait a long time to hear. Lots of people take a camera along with them on a vacation, but not many bring along a tape recorder!

If you have a tape recorder, use it like a camera to take a snapshot of sounds you hear. You can leave notes for yourself about the sounds, too, so you don't forget where and when you heard them. For example, if you record a lion's roar at the zoo, you can then record yourself saying, "That was a lion's roar from the San Diego Zoo. Monday, June 12."

Later you can turn your recordings into a game for other people. Play a sound and then stop the tape. Let them try to guess what it is. Then turn the tape back on and let them hear your notes about it.

THUMB WRESTLING

296

Use this "decider" game any time 2 people want the same thing, whether it's to ride in the front seat of the car or the last piece of dessert.

The object is to trap the other player's thumb beneath your thumb. Players hold out their right hands in a "thumbs-up" position. Link fingers, but keep your thumbs sticking up in the air. On the count of 3, try to pin the other player's thumb down by catching it and pressing it down with your own thumb. The person who wins 2 games out of 3 wins the contest.

MAKE A MEDLEY

Sing your own special melody by mastering the art of medleys.

A medley is a song made up of the words and tunes from different songs, sort of like a patchwork quilt that is sewn from the bits and pieces of other materials. Making your own medley is simple. Just start singing, and as soon as you think of another song, jump in with it.

If you have a couple of singing partners with you, try to string together as many songs as possible. See what funny combinations you can make. For example, can you sing the following wacky medley?

Yankee Doodle went to town a-riding on his pony . . .
. . . Whose fleece was white as snow. Everywhere that Mary went . . .
. . . all of the other reindeer used to laugh and call him names . . .
. . . all the livelong day. I've been working on the railroad, just to pass the time away . . .

WHAT'S THIS DITTY?

Turn off the radio for a change, and make your own melodies with this musical guessing game.

How many songs do you know? You'll find out after a few games of What's This Ditty? Players take turns humming a song or commercial jingle. See who is the fastest at figuring out songs.

RULES, RULES, RULES

299

You don't have to be a grown-up to make up a few rules of your own.

Before your trip, make your own "Wacky Rule Book." Ask each person in your family to make up one silly rule (the sillier the better), and write it down in your book. Everyone tries to follow these silly rules for the entire trip. Keep track of who obeys them the longest. The player who wins should get some reward, such as extra dessert for dinner.

Following are some very silly rules. See how many more you can invent.

—No one may use the word "yes." You have to say something like "of course," or "sure," or "you betcha" instead.

—You have to point with 2 fingers instead of 1.

—You have to use your left hand to put a straw into a drink. (If you're a left-handed person, you must use your right hand).

—Whenever a red car passes your car, you have to yell, "One-Ton Tomato!"

ROTATING ART

300

Here's a wacky drawing game that's perfect for 4 players.

You Will Need: Drawing paper, pencils

Fold your paper down in half. Then fold it down in half again. Now open it up and use the folds you made to refold it like an accordion.

Each person takes turns drawing part of a person or animal. The first person starts with the head. The second person draws shoulders to waist. The third person draws waist to knees, and the fourth person draws knees to feet. You may decide together what you're going to draw, or keep it a secret from each other until you're done. However you choose to do it, each person draws his or her part of the drawing secretly and then folds that part back behind the paper so the next person can't see what was drawn.

Draw your line partway into the next person's space so he or she knows where to continue drawing. When the last panel is completed, open all of the panels. It's almost certain that the result will be a very wacky drawing!

ROCK, PAPER, SCISSORS

This can be a "decider" game between 2 people competing for the same thing—or you can play it just for fun!

Players hold one fist in the air. On the count of 3, lower your arm quickly and "throw" a hand sign for rock, paper, or scissors, as shown. If both players throw the same sign, play again. Here's how to score.

—Scissors beat paper (by "cutting" the paper)

—Paper beats rock (by "wrapping" the rock)

—Rock beats scissors (by "dulling" the scissors)

Rock

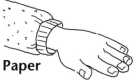

Paper

Scissors

THIS IS YOUR LIFE

Have you ever been someplace new and felt like you don't know anyone at all? Make a list of the people you know, and you'll never be alone again!

You Will Need: Paper, pencil

Without counting, see if you can guess how many people you know by name. Write the number down. Now make a list of the people you know.

It's easier if you keep a separate page for different people. For example, start with a page for family members, then another for all the friends you've ever had, then the kids and teachers you know from school, people from your neighborhood, your parents' friends, and so on. When you can't think of any more people that you know, count the names you wrote down. How close to your guess were you?

SHIRK SMIRK

Have you ever been told that you are good at "keeping a straight face" or that you have a good "poker face"? If so, you'll be great at Shirk Smirk.

The object of the game is simple enough: Don't laugh when someone asks you a question. That's not so hard, is it?

Not so fast! You have to answer every question, no matter what it is, by saying, "Stinky slippers." For example, you might be asked, "What did you eat for breakfast?" You have to answer "Stinky slippers." If someone asks, "Who is your best friend?" You have to answer, "Stinky slippers." How long can you last without laughing? If you win, think of a new funny answer and let someone else have a try.

TIC-TAC-TOE-TEE

304

If Tic-Tac-Toe isn't fun anymore, add a "Tee" and see what happens!

You Will Need: Pencil, paper

Tic-Tac-Toe-Tee (also known as Four Ts) is played just like Tic-Tac-Toe, but on a larger playing grid. The object is to get 4 in a row, not 3.

Draw 6 lines down and 6 lines across, making a grid of squares. Decide who will be X and who will be O. Players take turns putting their marks on the grid. The first person to get 4 in a row is the winner.

If you really like to play Four Ts, make your own special board by drawing the grid on a square piece of felt or cardboard. Then use 2 different colors of checkers or bottle caps instead of writing the letters.

ANGULAR LOGIC

305

Capture as many triangles as you can corner!

You Will Need: Paper, pencil

Make a grid of dots (8 across and 8 down makes a good game). Each player takes a turn by drawing 1 line that connects 2 dots. The object is to connect 2 lines with a third line to make a triangle.

When you create a triangle, write the first letter of your name inside it so you can count them all later. Play until there are no more dots to connect. The player with the most triangles wins. NOTE: Lines cannot cross each other.

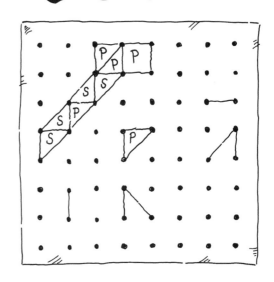

CARD COLLECTING

306

Collecting business cards is just as much fun as collecting stamps, and it's a surefire way to remember all the places you visited on your trip.

Nearly everyone has a business card. Some of them can be quite unusual. We have found clear plastic business cards, pop-up business cards, metal business cards, gigantic business cards—even a business card carved out of wood! You can find business cards everywhere: next to cash registers, pinned to bulletin boards, even stapled to brochures and papers.

You can collect business cards in many ways. The easiest way is to keep every single card you find. But you can also collect cards by theme, color, size, shape, or material. To store your cards, put them into a photo album, or tape them into a spiral notebook. If you want to make your collection last for a long time, you can get special business card albums from an office supply store.

CRAYON CAPER

307

Guess the color of a hidden crayon without ever looking at it!

You Will Need: 5 or 6 crayons

Put 5 or 6 crayons on the table. Tell your audience, "I can tell the color of things just by feeling them. I don't even need to look! I'll prove it with these crayons."

Turn your back, and put both your hands behind your back. Ask someone to pick a crayon and put it in your hand. With your hands still behind your back, turn around and face the audience again. Say, "I will now attempt to guess the color of the crayon without looking at it. But please be very quiet, because I need to concentrate." At the same time that you are saying this, use your fingernail to dig out a very small piece of the crayon.

When you finish saying the sentence, bring the hand that you used to dig out the crayon piece around the front and rub your forehead as if you're concentrating. Quickly, and without being obvious, take a peek at the color of the crayon that's under your fingernail. Rub your forehead for a few moments. Then put your hand behind your back again. Say, "I can feel the vibrations from the crayon telling me that the color is—" and say the color of the crayon. Bring the crayon from behind your back, and toss it on the table.

HOLE IN YOUR HAND

308

You don't need X-ray glasses to see right through the middle of your hand.

You Will Need: 1 piece of paper rolled into a tube

Pretend the tube is a telescope and look through the end, but keep both eyes open. Now hold your other hand up against the side of the tube. The hand should be flat, and your fingers should point up. If you have both eyes open, you will be able to see a hole magically appear in the middle of your hand!

SOLITAIRE #1

This solitaire game is great for playing in a car, plane, or train, because you don't have to lay the cards out on a table.

You Will Need: A deck of cards

Shuffle the deck, and take 3 cards off the top. Now take a look at the cards. If the first and third cards match each other in number or suit, you win the round and get to keep all 3 cards. If they don't match, you lose the round and forfeit all 3 cards. Make separate piles for each group.

Go through the entire deck of cards this way. You will have one card left over. Put it aside (let's say it's the 8 of clubs), because you'll need it for figuring out your score. First count the number of cards that you won in the game. You get 1 point for each. Add an additional point for every card that matches the suit of the card that was left over (in our example, clubs), and another point for each card that matches it in number (8). If you have 26 points or better, you win; if not, you lose.

ODD OR EVEN

This "decider" game is similar to Rock, Paper, Scissors (#301), but you can play it with 3 or more people.

Players each hold one fist in the air. On the count of 3, lower your arm quickly and "throw" out either 1, 2, 3, 4, or 5 fingers. At the same time, shout out "Odd!" or "Even!" Add up the total number of fingers on both your hands. The winner is the player who called out ODD or EVEN correctly. If both call it out correctly, play again.

For example, you throw out 3 fingers and call, "Odd!" Your friend throws out 5 fingers and calls, "Even!" 3 plus 5 is 8, which is an even number, so your friend wins.

HOW FAR, HOW FAST?

311

Have you ever wondered how long it would take to get somewhere if you had to ride your bike? Here's a great way to find out!

You Will Need: U.S. road atlas, ruler, pencil, paper

Be a navigator by figuring out how long it takes to travel from place to place. Start by measuring the distance between 2 cities in inches. Now look on your map for a "scale" that shows you how many miles equals 1 inch. Multiply that number by the number of inches you've measured. That will tell you about how many miles apart the 2 cities are. For example, measure 5 inches between cities. The scale says that every inch equals 10 miles. 5 times 10 equals 50, so the cities are about 50 miles apart.

But how long will it take you to get there by bike? Let's say you're riding 10 miles an hour. Then it would take you 5 hours to go 50 miles. If you go by car on the highway, you will drive about 50 miles an hour. How long will it take you to go 50 miles at that speed? One hour! If you travel by high-speed train, you'll zoom along at about 100 miles an hour. That's twice as fast as a car, so you'll get their twice as quickly. Going 50 miles at 100 miles an hour will only take you half an hour.

Can you figure out how fast it will take you to get from one city to the next by bike, car, and train?

San Francisco, California, to Sacramento, California
New York City, New York, to Los Angeles, California
Miami, Florida to Portland, Maine
Chicago, Illinois, to New Orleans, Louisiana
Sante Fe, New Mexico, to Butte, Montana
Seattle, Washington, to Atlanta, Georgia

TRAVEL TRIVIA

Wyoming was the first state to grant women the right to vote. It did so in 1869, even before Wyoming had achieved official statehood.

MAKE A CUP

312

Just add water, and you're ready to quench your thirst!

You Will Need: A square piece of paper (notebook paper is fine)

Fold the paper in half diagonally, as shown (Picture 1). Next, fold the right bottom corner up (Picture 2), then fold the left bottom corner up (Picture 3). Now fold one top flap toward you, the other one away from you (Picture 4). Squeeze the edges inward and open up your cup (Picture 5). Fill with water and take a sip!

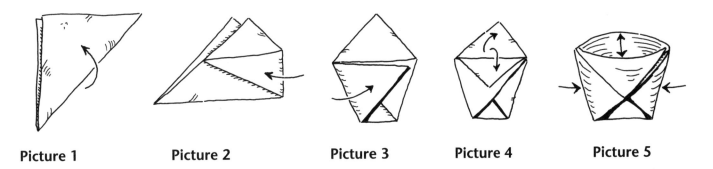

Picture 1   **Picture 2**   **Picture 3**   **Picture 4**   **Picture 5**

GUESSTIMATE

313

Here's a car game that everyone can play—except the driver!

You Will Need: Paper, pen or pencil

Ask whomever is driving to set the car's trip odometer to zero (or to tell you the current mileage reading so you can write it down). Then ask the driver to check the speedometer to see how many miles per hour he or she is traveling. Based on that information, each player must guess how many miles will be covered in the next 10, 20, and 30 minutes. Write down everyone's guesses. As each time period is reached, ask the driver for a new mileage reading, and see which of the players guessed closest to the actual amount.

Keep in mind that playing the game during highway travel is much easier than playing it while driving on city streets, where there are stoplights, pedestrians, and slower-moving traffic to deal with. Still, you can never be sure what effects may be caused by weather and traffic conditions.

INITIAL GAME

The object of this game is to think of real names to match up with a random list of initials.

You Will Need: Paper, pencil

```
A T =
B H =   Bob Hope
C E =
D E =
E A =
F R =
G L =
H Y =
I B =
J I =
K R =
L D =
M C =
N A =
O T =
P C =
Q H =
R E =
S T =
T T =
U H =
V E =
W W =
X O =
Y R =
Z M =
```

Each player writes the letters of the alphabet, A through Z, down one side of a piece of paper. Then, someone thinks of a famous saying, book title, or song title that has at least 26 letters in it—for example, "The early bird catches the worm." Each player then writes down the first 26 letters of the phrase—leaving no spaces between words—next to the alphabet column, so you have all made the same pairs of initials.

To play, each player has to think of a famous person, book character, cartoon character, or movie character who has the initials you have put on your page. You can set a time limit if you want, but this game really isn't a race. In our puzzle, for example, the letters BH could stand for Bob Hope, the famous comedian.

If more than one person thought of a name for the same initials, but the names are different, each player scores 1 point. Score no points if someone else thought of the same name that you did; however, if you thought of a name for a pair of initials but no one else did, you score 5 points! The player with the highest score wins.

TRAVEL TRIVIA

The Appalachian Trail, the world's longest walking route, passes through 14 states along its 2,144-mile route from Springer Mountain in Georgia to Mount Katahdin in Maine.

TIC-TAC-MATH

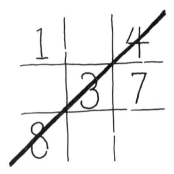

By adding a few numbers, you can turn an old game into something new!

You Will Need: Pencil, paper

Draw a normal Tic-Tac-Toe board (2 lines down, 2 lines across). Instead of using X or O, players take turns putting in a number between 1 and 9. The winner is the person who fills in a third square—but only if that row adds up to 15! Numbers can only be used one time per game.

TRAVEL TRIVIA
Built in 1830, Baltimore's Mount Clare Station was the first railroad station in the United States. Today it is part of the B&O Railroad Museum.

BROKEN CRAYON

Here's a trick that proves that sounds can be deceiving!

You Will Need: A crayon

Place the crayon lengthwise near the edge of a table. Pretend to pick it up with both hands, curling your fingers underneath it as if you are going to break it in half. Before you actually pick up the crayon, however, use your fingers to push the crayon off the table and onto your lap–carefully, so no one sees you do it. (You may want to practice this move a few times before trying it in front of an audience.)

Now bring your hands up (still pretending to hold the crayon) and pretend to snap the crayon in half. You can make a sound that sounds like a crayon breaking by snapping one thumbnail off the other as you bring your hands apart. Keep your fists closed, as if you're holding the pieces of crayon. Then, open your hands to show that the crayon has vanished!

BASKETBALL SIGNS

Even if you're not a serious basketball fan, see if you can match the list of referee signals with the appropriate drawing. (Answers on page 236.)

Traveling
Score
Technical foul
Stop the clock
Start the clock

EEP-OPP-ORK-AHA

The faster you play this card-matching game, the funnier it gets.

You Will Need: A deck of cards

Deal out all the cards, one at a time, to all players. It doesn't matter if some players end up with one more card than the others. Play goes in a clockwise circle starting with the person on the dealer's left.

Player 1 takes any one of his or her cards and places it faceup in the middle of the table. At the same time, he or she calls out "Eep!" If Player 2 has a card of the same number or rank, he or she places it faceup in the middle of the table and shouts "Opp!" (If Player 2 doesn't have a matching card, he or she says "Pass.")

The third player with a matching card lays it down on the table and shouts "Ork!" The fourth player to do so shouts "Aha!" The person who plays the fourth card starts the next round by laying down a new card and shouting "Eep!"

NOTE: If a player has more than one matching card, he or she must play them all in the same turn, saying the correct word for each card he or she lays down. The winner is the person who manages to play all of his or her cards.

WHAT'S MY NUMBER?

319

Guess your opponent's number, and you'll be rewarded.

You Will Need: Paper, pencils

Before the game, each player draws the following scoring grid on his or her page:

```
8 8 8 8 8 8 8
7 7 7 7 7 7 7
6 6 6 6 6 6
5 5 5 5 5
4 4 4 4
3 3 3
2 2
1
```

To start the game, Player 1 writes down a secret number from 1 to 8. Player 2 tries to guess the number that Player 1 wrote down. If Player 2 guesses correctly, he or she gets to cross that number off on the scoring grid. If Player 2 guesses incorrectly, the player who wrote the secret number gets to cross it off the scorecard. Take turns going back and forth, guessing and crossing out numbers. The player who crosses out all of his or her numbers first is the winner.

BACKWARD BREATHING

320

Getting your mind and body to think in 2 different directions at once can be tough. Can you do it?

Breathe in and out. Pay close attention to how your tummy and chest move. As you breathe IN, your tummy and chest move OUT. As you breathe OUT, your tummy and chest move IN.

Now try breathing out, but make it look like you're breathing in. Then try breathing in, but make it look like you're breathing out. Sounds easy, but it's a hard thing to do!

WHO, WHAT, WHERE?

321

How much can you guess about people just by watching?

Here's a quiet people-watching activity to do when you find yourself waiting around an airport, shopping mall, or some other crowded place. All the action takes place in your head, so no one even knows you're playing a game!

Look around at people in the crowd. Based on what people are carrying or wearing, can you guess the following: What do they do for a living? How old are they? Where do they live? What are their names? Are they married? What's their favorite sport? What's their favorite food? Do they have any pets?

Of course, you'll never really know the answer to these questions. But if someone you're with likes to play this game, it can be interesting to see what kind of different answers you both think up!

SURROUNDED!

322

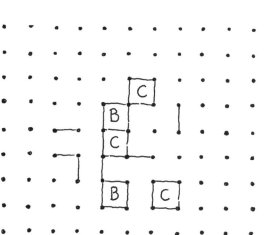

The object of this game is to make as many squares as you can by connecting the dots, one turn at a time.

You Will Need: Paper, 2 pencils

Before you play, make a grid of 10 dots across and 10 dots down, all about ½ inch apart. Each player takes turns connecting 2 dots with a single line. Connect up or down, but not diagonally.

When you finish a box by drawing the fourth "wall," put your initial inside it. When all of the dots are connected, count up and see who made the most squares. You can make the game longer or shorter by adding more dots or taking some away.

WAY BACK WHEN

Can you figure out what happened way back when?

50 years ago . . .
Would you be able to watch television?
Would you be able to play on your computer?
Had anybody walked on the moon yet?
Would you listen to music on a radio, a tape player, or a CD player?
Would you be able to go mountain biking?
Would you use a microwave oven or a gas stove to cook food?

100 years ago . . .
How would your family travel on vacation?
What would you have done in the summers?
What kind of clothes would you have worn?
Would you have been able to call your friends on the phone?
How would people get messages to other people?

1,000 years ago . . .
Would you have parks to play in?
What type of school would you have gone to?
What would your favorite food have been?
What would you want to be when you grew up?
What kind of pet would you have had?
What kind of jobs would your parents have?
Would you have lived in the United States?

DISAPPEARING COIN

Count to 3, and the coin will vanish before their eyes!

You Will Need: A coin

Have a friend stand facing you with his left hand out. Show him the coin and say, "I am going to touch your hand three times with this coin. The third time, I want you to take the coin from me as fast as you can. Watch your hand as closely as you can so you don't miss it!"

Bring the coin up high by your ear. Bring it down, and as you count ONE, touch his palm with the coin. Bring the coin up again by your ear and bring it down again, counting TWO as the coin touches his palm. Move your hand up by your ear again, but this time drop the coin into your shirt collar. (Practice this so you can do it without pausing at all. And make sure your shirt is tucked in or the coin will fall out, ruining your trick.)

Now bring your hand down and touch your friend's palm again, counting THREE. Your friend will close his hand, trying to catch the coin. Show that both your hands are empty, and have him open his. The coin has vanished!

TANGRAM

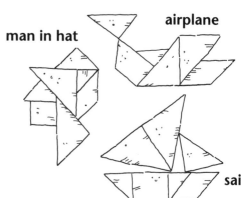

man in hat

airplane

sailboat

Can you figure out the patterns by moving your tangrams?

You Will Need: Tangram from Chapter 1 (see #8)

Use the shapes in your tangram kit to make the shapes below. What other shapes can you invent? Draw your tangram shapes and give them to someone else to try to solve.

SPACE RACE

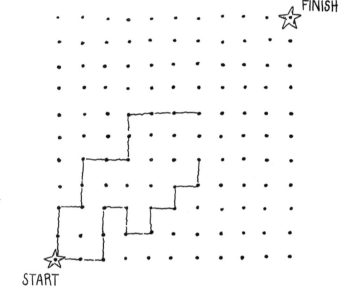

Be the first to fly across the galaxy!

You Will Need: Paper, different colored markers or crayons, dice or spinner (see #1)

The object of this game is to race from one corner of the galaxy to the other. Draw a grid of dots (at least 10 down and 10 across) on your page. These are the "stars" in the galaxy. Mark one corner star "Start" and its opposite corner star "Finish."

Players take turns making lines between stars. Before drawing a line, however, a player must roll the dice or spin the spinner. If the number is EVEN, you must draw a line to the left. If the number is ODD, you must draw a line to the right. The first one to get to the end wins. Players must also follow these special rules:

• Players make only 1 line per turn.
• Players can't cross each other's lines.
• If you can't move because you'll cross paths, wait for your next turn.

JINGLE JANGLES

Did you ever stop to think about all the songs you hear during commercials? They're called "jingles." How many commercial jingles can you sing?

If you were trying to create a song to describe your favorite food, bike, clothes, car, or toy, what would you say about it? Take a popular tune and make up new words to promote your favorite object. How would you get people to buy it? Can you make a message that rhymes? How about making up your own tune for your new jingle?

GOPHERS

Block the other gopher's tunnel, and dig your own tunnel all the way across the yard!

You Will Need: Paper, different colored markers or crayons

Make a grid of dots at least 10 across and 10 down. This is the "yard." Gophers start on opposite sides of the grid board. Take turns drawing lines from dot to dot, 1 per turn. These lines are the "tunnels."

Tunnels may not cross each other. The object of the game is to get your tunnel all the way across the yard from one side to the other, while blocking the other gopher's tunnel. The first gopher to reach the other side wins.

REMINDERS

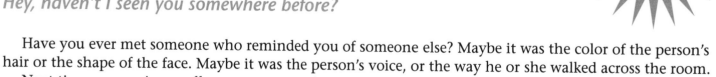

328

329

Hey, haven't I seen you somewhere before?

Have you ever met someone who reminded you of someone else? Maybe it was the color of the person's hair or the shape of the face. Maybe it was the person's voice, or the way he or she walked across the room.

Next time you are in a mall, amusement park, or another place with lots of people around, take a long look at the people around you. See if you can find people who remind you of your parents, friends—or even yourself! How many "familiar faces" can you find?

CARTOON CAPER

You don't need a TV to see cartoons whenever you want!

You Will Need: Sheet of notebook paper cut into 3 long strips, pencil

Fold a strip of paper in half. On the bottom flap, draw a cartoon that shows half of a simple action—for example, a person sitting in a chair. On the top flap, show the other half of the action; for example, a person standing in front of a chair (Picture 1). Now roll the upper flap tightly around a pencil to give it a strong curl (Picture 2).

Hold the upper corner flat against the table, and move the pencil rapidly up and down as shown to make the flap unroll and roll up again. If you do it fast enough, it looks like a cartoon of a person sitting and standing over and over again (Picture 3). You can draw anything you like: a dog running, a face smiling, a ball bouncing, and so on. How many cartoon books can you create?

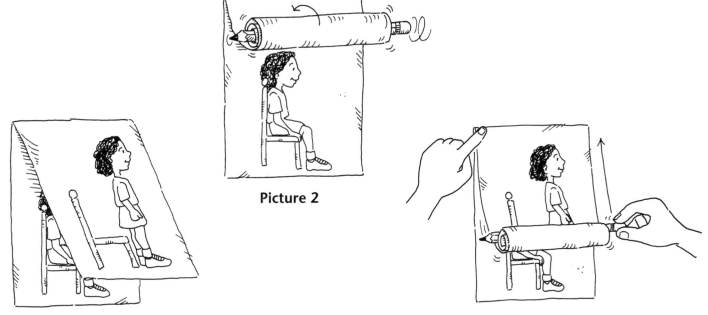

Picture 2

Picture 1

Picture 3

LINKED CLIPS

A quick flip of the wrist, and two separate paper clips become linked together—it's magic!

You Will Need: 2 paper clips, dollar bill

Fold over about one-third of the dollar bill away from you as shown. Don't crease the fold. Clip it with a paper clip (Picture 1). Fold the other end of the paper toward you. Clip it as shown (Picture 2).

Pull the ends of the dollar bill apart sharply and the 2 paper clips will leap into the air. (With practice, you can make them jump straight up so you can catch them as they fall.) Show them to the audience. Two separate paper clips have mysteriously become linked together as one (Picture 3).

Picture 1

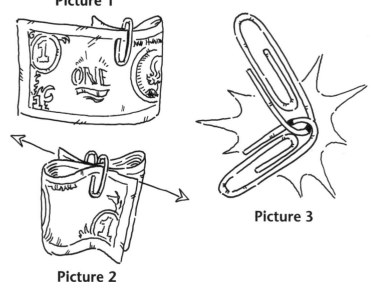

Picture 2

Picture 3

RHYTHM JAM

This is a little like rubbing your stomach and patting your head—only you're keeping a beat and thinking of new words.

Start by naming a category (such as places to visit, types of food, or kinds of trees). Then, start the following beat: Slap your hands on your lap twice, then clap twice, and then snap twice. Once you're through, repeat and keep going until everybody is keeping a steady rhythm together.

Now, each player takes his or her turn naming something in the category chosen. The trick is, you have to name it while snapping, and no words can be said twice. Miss the beat and you're out.

TORN-UP COIN TRICK

333

Fold a piece of paper around a coin. Say the magic words and tear up the paper. The coin has vanished!

You Will Need: A coin, a 4-inch-square piece of paper

The secret is in the way the paper is folded. Take the paper and place a coin just below the center (Picture 1). Fold the bottom of the paper up over the coin (Picture 2). Now pick the paper up and fold the top part away from you (Picture 3). Now fold in the 2 sides, also away from you (Picture 4).

It will look as if the coin is safely folded inside the small paper packet. But unknown to your audience, the top edge of the packet is open. Take the packet in your right hand by the top, and turn it over as you do so. You can now let the coin slip out of the packet and into your hand without anyone noticing (Picture 5). Tear up the paper, keeping the coin hidden in your hand. To the audience, it looks as if you have made the coin vanish into thin air! Put the pieces of paper in your pocket and drop the coin there, too.

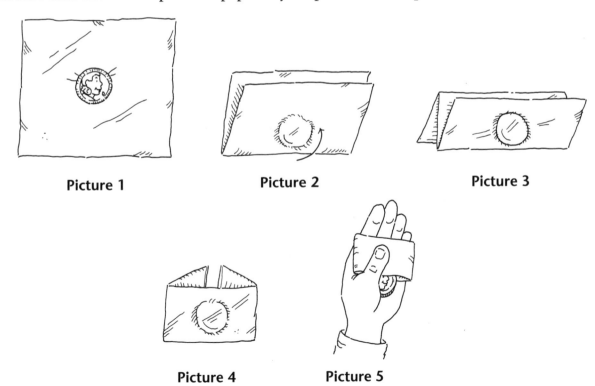

Picture 1

Picture 2

Picture 3

Picture 4

Picture 5

COIN CAPER

This disappearing coin trick works because the coin doesn't disappear!

You Will Need: A coin, salt or pepper shaker, paper napkin

This is a surprise magic trick, because the audience thinks the coin is going to disappear—but in the end, you make the saltshaker disappear instead!

To do this trick, you must be seated at a table. Place the coin on the table. Say, "I am going to make this coin disappear without touching it with my hands." Then cover the coin with the saltshaker. Say, "So you can't see my magic, I'm going to cover the whole thing with a napkin." Unfold the napkin and place it over the saltshaker. Without tearing the napkin, push it down around the saltshaker. Say, "One, two, three!" Then move the saltshaker and napkin toward your body, to the very edge of the table. The coin is still there, of course, because you haven't done anything yet.

Now you say, "Hmmm. That's odd. It should have worked. Let me try it again. One, two, three!" On three, move the saltshaker and napkin to the very edge of the table again. The coin is still there. Say, "Gee, I'm kind of embarrassed. This worked when I practiced it! One more time. One, two, three!" On three, move the saltshaker and napkin toward you again, but this time drop the saltshaker silently off the edge of the table into your lap. Keep your legs together so the shaker doesn't fall to the floor. In your hand you now have an empty napkin, but it still looks as though you are holding the saltshaker!

Say, "Oh! Now I know why this isn't working. It's not the coin that was supposed to disappear. It was the saltshaker!" As soon as you say "saltshaker," slam your other hand down on top of the napkin with a bang. The saltshaker has vanished!

TRAVEL TRIVIA

The tallest sand dunes in the world are found at the base of Colorado's Sangre de Cristo Mountains. Covering 39 square miles, the wind-whipped dunes rise as high as 700 feet.

FLOATING KNIFE

A butter knife floats in the air—with nothing to hold it up!

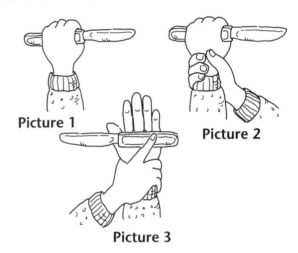

Picture 1

Picture 2

Picture 3

Take a butter knife (a drinking straw or pencil will work, too) in your left fist (Picture 1). Grasp your left wrist with your right hand (Picture 2). Now slowly open the fingers of your left hand, and the butter knife will stay where it is, as if it's stuck to your hand with a magnet!

You know the trick, of course. When you grasp your left wrist, you secretly extend your right pointer finger. It's your finger, and not magic or magnets, that holds the butter knife in place (Picture 3)!

TONK

The object of this card game is to get rid of high cards and collect low cards. The player with the lowest number of points wins.

You Will Need: A deck of cards

Deal 5 cards to each player. Put the rest of the deck in the center, facedown. Turn over the top card and place it next to the deck. This is the discard pile.

The player to the left of the dealer can draw a card from the top of the discard pile or take a new one from the facedown deck. After drawing a card, he or she must discard 1. Players can hold only 5 cards at a time. The idea is to keep low cards and discard high cards. Numbered cards count for their face value. Face cards (jack, queen, and king) count as 10 points. Aces count as 1 point.

As soon as a player's cards total 21 points or less, he or she yells "Tonk!" and lays down the hand to show the other players. The winner scores zero points (remember, the lowest score wins), while the other players are stuck with the total points of the 5 cards they are holding. Keep playing new hands until all but one player has accumulated 100 or more points. That player is the winner.

VERBAL REMEDIES

337

This guessing game will tickle your funny bone!

One player is chosen to be the doctor who knows of a wonderful new exercise for people who are sick. Maybe it's running, or skiing, or swimming, or skydiving—it can be any activity. The "doctor" decides on the activity and keeps it to himself.

Now it is up to the rest of the players to figure out what the doctor's miracle cure is by asking the doctor YES or NO questions. The only thing is, every time they ask a question, the doctor responds with a funny verb (the doctor picks a silly verb and uses it every time a question is answered). For example, a question and answer might go something like this. The doctor is thinking of the activity mountain biking. "Doctor, can you do this remedy in the water?" The doctor responds, "No, you can't flubber in the water."

Obviously, "flubbering" isn't the remedy—but it is up to the rest of the players to figure out what the doctor really means by saying "flubbering." The first one to figure out the doctor's remedy gets to be the next doctor.

Other questions might be, "Doctor, do you need special equipment for your remedy?" The doctor says, "Yes, to flubber you need special equipment," and so on until someone guesses. The person who correctly guesses the remedy gets to be the doctor next.

TEMPO

338

Imagine leading the performance of dozens of musicians, just by moving your hands. You can play Tempo with just about any song you like to sing.

Choose someone to be the conductor. Now pick a song to sing that everyone knows. The conductor must softly tap or clap out the rhythm of the song. Everyone must sing the song along with this rhythm. But the conductor can change the speed (or "tempo") whenever he or she wants to—fast or slow or in-between. You have to change the speed of your singing to match the conductor's tempo. Who in your group is best at keeping up with the conductor?

SOUND OFF

Here's a story that let's everyone get into the act!

Pick someone to read this story aloud. Whenever the reader reads one of the words that are in capital letters, he or she should point to the people who are listening. That's everyone else's cue to make a noise for that word. You can use your voice to make noises, or clap your hands, or tap your feet—whatever you like.

For example, the reader might say, "We saw a big DOG," and then point to the listeners on the word DOG. The listeners should then bark like a dog—or howl, or pant, or make whatever dog noise they can think of. Listeners should make sound effects for every word in capital letters. Let the noise begin!

Lucky was a tabby CAT who lived in an old barn with a HORSE, a COW, a DONKEY, a ROOSTER, and an old DOG. One day Lucky the CAT was WALKING outside the barn when he saw two MICE. Lucky was a very curious CAT. When he saw that the MICE were TALKING, he tiptoed up behind them to listen.

"We have to get rid of that CAT," said the first MOUSE, MUNCHING on a carrot. "He never lets us have any fun."

"You're right," said the second MOUSE, SIPPING a glass of lemonade. "That CAT won't let us SING. He won't let us talk on the PHONE. He won't let us RUN. He won't even let us SWIM, which is what MICE like to do best!"

"Tonight we'll have a meeting in the barn when everyone else is ASLEEP," said the first MOUSE. "We'll decide what to do with that CAT once and for all! Tell all the MICE to meet in the DONKEY'S stall at MID-NIGHT."

That night, as the OWL hooted in the tree, Lucky the CAT hid behind the COW to spy on the MICE. He waited and waited, but the MICE never showed up. A CRICKET on the wall said, "Look out behind you!"

Lucky the CAT turned around and saw hundreds of MICE all lined up behind him. Some of the MICE carried TRUMPETS. Some carried RATTLES. Some carried FIRECRACKERS. Some carried BELLS. And all of them were singing, "HAPPY BIRTHDAY" to Lucky the CAT.

Lucky was so happy that he WHOOPED with delight. "That's what I get for being too curious."

ADD IT UP AGAIN!

340

This trick will fool your friends—and even you, the first time you play it!

Take a small scrap of paper and cover up the list of numbers below. Uncover the numbers one at a time from the top down. Add them up in your head, starting with 1,000 and ending with 10. What answer did you get? People usually say 5,000. But guess what? It's not! The correct answer is 4,100! When you play this trick on your friends and family, cover up the numbers for them. Have them add the numbers out loud as you uncover them one by one. How many people get the correct answer the first time?

1000
40
1000
30
1000
20
1000
10

THIS EQUALS THAT

341

You won't find any arithmetic in these "math" puzzles!

On one side of the = sign is a number. On the other side is the first letter of the important words in a phrase or saying. For example, "24 = H. in a D." translates into "24 = Hours in a Day." Similarly, "10 = F. on your H." translates into "10 = Fingers on your Hands." Can you figure out the rest? Answers on page 236.

1 = N. on your F.	26 = L. in the A.
2 = E. in your H.	36 = I. in a Y.
4 = Q. in a G.	52 = C. in a D.
6 = S. on a G.	100 = Y. in a C.
9 = P. in the S. S.	365 = D. in a Y.
12 = D. of C.	5,280 = F. in a M.
12 = E. in a D.	20,000 = L. under the S.

HELPING HAND

Two hands are better than one—or are they?

You Will Need: Pencil, paper

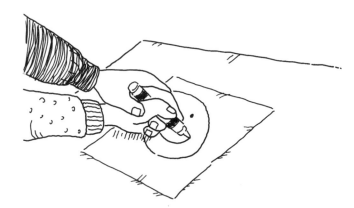

Whether you are right-handed or left-handed, have you ever tried to draw with your opposite hand? Pretty hard, isn't it? Well, here's something even trickier: Try to draw with someone else's hand!

Grasp a friend's hand the same way you would when you clasp your own hands together. With your other hand, place a pencil between the pointer fingers and middle fingers of both your hands, as shown. Now decide on a picture you both want to draw. Try something simple first, like a smiley face. Talk aloud about what parts you want to draw.

Once you get the hang of it, try using your hands without talking. You can also write a sentence, or for some crazy fun, don't decide on anything out loud—just start drawing together and see what you can come up with!

SIGN-ALONG

A sign-along is like a sing-along, but with a twist

343

In ancient times, before everyone knew how to read and write, people kept track of history through songs. Songs were easy to remember and teach to other people. Sometimes, when songs were sung at large gatherings, hand signs were added. Today you might see musical groups adding hand signs to their songs as they sing them for fun.

In a sign-along, you pick a song and think of as many hand signs to go along with the song as you can. For example, if you sing "Mary Had a Little Lamb," you could make up a hand sign for "Mary" (gesture for long hair) and for "Lamb" (make a lamb out of the fingers of your hand).

Now sing the song all the way through, adding the hand signs. Can you get all the way through without forgetting a sign?

SINGING IN ROUNDS

344

It's hard to sing a square, but singing rounds is easy as can be!

Singing together in rounds can be a simple way to change a melody and make any song sound even prettier. If you have more than 2 people, divide yourselves into 2 groups to start, trying to balance out the voices.

Let's use a song everybody knows for an example. The first person (or group) starts off by singing "Mary had a little lamb, little lamb, little lamb." Then, as that person (or group) begins the second line ("Whose fleece was white as snow"), the second person (or group) starts singing the first line again. Keep going until the end of the song.

Two other good songs to sing in rounds:

Twinkle Twinkle, little star
How I wonder what you are.
Up above the world so bright,
Like a candle in the night,
Twinkle Twinkle, little star
How I wonder what you are.

I've been working on the railroad, all the livelong day
I've been working on the railroad, just to pass
*   the time away*
Can't you hear the whistle blowing, rise up so early
*   in the morn*
Can't you hear the captain shouting, Dinah blow your horn.
Dinah won't you blow, Dinah won't you blow, Dinah won't you
*   blow your horn.*

STATUES

345

Be careful playing this outdoor game. Birds might think you're a real statue and try to make a nest on your head!

Choose 1 person to be the Statue Maker. Everybody else marches around, jumping, strutting, and acting as wild and crazy as possible. When the Statue Maker calls "Statues!" players must freeze in whatever position they may be in at the time. Hold your positions as long as you can. If you move, you're out of the game. The last one to stay completely still gets to be Statue Maker next game.

MASKLESS MASKS

Can you say the opposite of what you feel and look the opposite of what you say? It isn't easy!

Some things you do go hand in hand—such as laughing and smiling, frowning and sounding mad. It's just the way our faces work. But can you reverse that by wearing a Maskless Mask? Try these:

- Smile as big as you can, but say something with an angry voice. You might pretend you just had something hot spilled on your lap.

- Open your eyes as big as you can and bare your teeth (as if you were scared), but then try talking in a smooth, slow voice. Pretend you're talking to a baby that won't go to sleep.

- Relax every muscle in your face. Make no expression at all. Now, without moving your face, make your voice as excited as you can—describe your first ride on a rollercoaster, or the last game in the World Series as your team wins the title.

To test if you're really good, try this: Have one person watch you while another person keeps his or her eyes closed and listens. See if the person who is listening can tell you which emotion you're expressing.

MAKE ENVELOPES

Don't throw away all those printed materials you collect on vacation. Here's a better idea!

You Will Need: A variety of printed materials (such as maps, placemats, brochures, etc.), scissors, ruler, clear tape

If the printed document is much larger than an average sheet of paper, cut it down into a rectangle shape (longer on one side, shorter on the other). A sheet of notebook paper (8½×11 inches) is a good size to practice with.

Pick which side you want to be on the outside of your envelope. Lay that side facedown against the table, and position so that the longer side of the paper goes from left to right. Fold up the bottom 4 inches of the paper and crease well (Picture 1). Then fold the sides over about half an inch, using tape to seal them in place (Picture 2). After you've finished your letter and put it inside, close and seal the remaining flap (Picture 3). Put the postage, the address you're sending the letter to, and your return address on the other side of the envelope. Use address labels if your envelope is too dark to read easily or is difficult to write on.

Picture 1

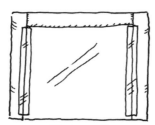

Picture 2

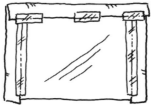

Picture 3

SONG DOWN

347

348

Here's a great singing game for long car trips.

How many songs can you think of that have the names of colors in their lyrics? Think of a basic color—green, for example. Then see how many songs you can think of that have the word green in them. For example, "It's Not Easy Being Green" or "Greensleeves."

See how long you can keep singing, with all the players adding on songs as they think of them. The person who thinks of the last song gets to pick the next color to sing about. Once you've sung the whole rainbow, pick other special words to sing about, such as people's names or animals, or all the songs with the word "love" in the title, and so on.

TRAFFIC SOUNDS

Here's a fun way to pass some time on the highway.

First, make a list of all the different sounds that you might hear on the highway and the conditions that cause these sounds. You can even make up sounds for different things you might see—for example, you could make a sneeze the sound required whenever you pass a hospital. (See our list below for some ideas.)

Every time one of the conditions is met, make the noise that goes with it. For example, when a car passes, you say, "Honk-honk!" When a truck passes, you say, "Varooom!" Soon you'll have the funniest sounding game on 4 wheels. The game really gets wild when everything starts happening at once!

Truck passes (varoooom!)
Convertible passes (beep-beep!)
Car passes (honk-honk!)
Police car or ambulance passes (siren noise)
Car goes over a bridge (rattle-rattle!)

You pass a speed limit sign (zoooom!)
You stop at a stop sign (screeech!)
You pass some cows (moooo!)
You pass a restaurant (eating noise)
You pass a gas station (glug-glug-glug)

IMPOSSIBLE KNOT TRICK

It's impossible for your friends to tie a knot in a string without letting go of the ends. But you can do it any time you want.

You Will Need: Piece of string about 2 feet long

Hand your friend a piece of string and ask him to tie a knot in it. But there's a catch: He's not allowed to let go of the ends! Try as he might, he won't be able to do it. But you can! Here's how.

Lay the string out on a table. Cross your arms and pick up the one end of string in each hand. By uncrossing your arms, a knot will form in the middle of the rope—and you didn't let go of the ends!

FOOTBALL SIGNS

Try your "hand" at football. Match the list of signals with the appropriate drawing. (Answers on page 236.)

Time out
Touchdown
Safety
Interference
Holding

SOLITAIRE #2

Here's another great card game for one person that can easily be played in a car, plane, or train.

You Will Need: A deck of cards

Hold the deck facedown in your left hand. Take the cards off the bottom of the deck, one at a time. Just before you turn over each card, count to yourself, "Ace, two, three, four," and so on, through King, one word for each card you turn over.

The object is to get through the entire deck without actually saying the name of the card you're about to turn over. For example, if you say "Nine" just before you turn over the 9 of clubs, the game is over. Count the number of cards you have turned up, and that's your score. Can you get through all 52 cards?

WHEN YOU GET HOME

A vacation doesn't have to end as soon as you get home. Keep the memories of your travels alive with these fun projects that will always remind you of the places you visited and the good times you had. Most of the activities involve making things from items collected during your travels—leaves, flowers, seashells, brochures, ticket stubs, postcards, and so on. For that reason, it's a good idea to skim through this section before your trip starts so that you have a better idea of the kinds of materials you'll be looking for.

 # RHYTHM STORIES

353

Make your own rhythm story to tell about your travels.

Start by thinking about rhythm. When you speak a sentence in a talking voice, it sounds much different than a rap sentence. Why? It all has to do with rhythm. Think of words as drums that can make 2 sounds—loud and long or soft and short. The sentence below is written with the long, loud beats in capital letters. Try saying it out loud with rhythm.

Now HERE'S a little STORy that I'd LIKE to SHARE,
about GOing to my GRANDma's house and SEEing a BEAR!

Now think about rhyme. Some words rhyme better than others. So when you are thinking about what you want to say, start by picking out the special words from your story and seeing what else you can rhyme them with. For example, if you want to talk about the nice place you went to visit, don't use the word "restaurant." That's too hard to rhyme! But you can talk about the "place we went to eat" because "eat" is much easier to rhyme.

Ready to give it a try?

STORYBOOKS

354

How many different stories can you show and tell about your trip?

You Will Need: Photos from your trip, Post-it notes, 2 different colored pens

Choose 10 to 20 of your favorite photos from your last trip, and lay them all out in front of you. Arrange the photos in the order that they were taken, and write a caption on a Post-it note for each picture. Put the top sticky part of the Post-it note along the bottom edge of the snapshot.

Read through the pictures in order to see what your first story looks and sounds like. Now put another blank Post-it note on top of each of the others. This time make up the silliest story you can think of, putting funny captions on new Post-it notes. This story can be completely made up. For example, the REAL story might be that your family went to the beach and played on the sand. But your MADE-UP story might be about how you flew in a rocket to Mars and spent your day in the Martian sand looking for alien creatures!

STORY MAP

355

Maps can tell you where to go and how to get there—but they can also tell what you saw and did, too!

You Will Need: Paper, crayons, road map

While looking at a road map, draw a rough outline of the trip you took with your family. It doesn't have to be an exact match; just concentrate on the roads and cities you traveled through, not every single thing on the map. Now think about what you saw as you traveled through each place. Corn? Cows? A big cactus? The ocean? Draw them on the map near the places where you saw them.

What did you do when you arrived? Did you camp in a tent? Eat a hamburger? See a circus? Walk around a museum? Draw a small picture of the most fun or most interesting things about your trip. When you're done, somebody else should be able to look at your map and see where you've been and what you've seen without ever reading a word!

PICTURE FRAMES

Turn a boring picture frame into a special reminder of your trip!

You Will Need: Shells, rocks, white glue, picture frame mat board, string, tape, scissors

Experiment with how you want to decorate your frame. Use anything you can glue down—pieces of maps, small shells, dried flowers, pictures, and so on.

Once you have a general idea of what you want it to look like, carefully glue everything in place. Let your frame dry overnight. Next, tape the picture you want to frame to the back so you can see it through the front. Cut a small piece of string about 4 inches long, and tape it to the back of your frame so you can hang it on a wall.

BOOKMARKS

Here's a neat bookmark you can make using pressed flowers.

You Will Need: Flowers found during your trip, felt or paper, white glue, soft wide paintbrush

Follow the directions for pressing flowers and leaves (see #87), then cut a piece of felt or stiff paper about 1½×6 inches. Arrange your dried flowers and leaves into a pretty pattern, and carefully glue them to the paper or felt.

Once the glue has dried, you can finish your bookmark one of two ways. Either have Mom or Dad help you seal it between 2 pieces of clear contact paper, or do the next step: Put enough white glue in the bottom of a paper cup to cover it. Add about the same amount of water to the glue. Stir it with your brush. Very gently, brush this glue mixture on top of your bookmark. Cover the paper, the flowers, and all the leaves. When the glue dries, it will leave a thin, protective coating that looks shiny.

358 NATURE SPATTERS

You can make your own nature stencils with things you find on your trip.

You Will Need: Newspaper, poster paint, old toothbrush, small cup full of water, white or colored paper, objects found outdoors (rocks, sticks, leaves, flowers, etc.)

Cover your work area with plenty of newspaper. Put different colors of poster paints into small flat dishes (saucers work well). Lay out a blank piece of white or colored paper on the newspaper. Place a few leaves on top of the blank paper, flattening them out.

Lightly dip the bristles of an old toothbrush into the paint. Use the brush to spatter the paint all over the paper, and all over the leaves, too. Rinse the brush in water before changing colors. When you lift up the leaves, you will see a blank area where the paint could not reach. Leave it like this, or draw in your own leaf using markers or crayons. What other objects make good stencils?

MOSAICS 359

Mosaics are pictures or patterns made out of small pieces of glass, stone, or tile. Make a mosaic using photos or brochures you found on your trip.

You Will Need: Colored paper (extra photos, postcards, and brochures are best), white glue, 1 sheet of heavy paper (8×8 inches)

Cut up extra photos, postcards, or brochures into small pieces about the size of a nickel. Make them all different shapes. Lay out the different pieces on your heavy paper so that the paper is completely covered. Move the pieces around until you like the pattern. Don't try to make a real picture out of it. Just look for good color and shape combinations.

Carefully glue each piece into place. If you want, you can cut your mosaic into a star, circle, or other shape after it's dry, and hang it in your room.

SHADOW BOX

A shadow box (or diorama) is a type of sculpture in which a miniature scene is created that looks like a place you've seen in real life.

You Will Need: Shoe box, glue, paper, scissors, paints or crayons, found objects (rocks, sticks, leaves, flowers, brochures, etc.)

To make your own diorama, start by cutting a piece of paper to fit in the back of an old shoe box. Color or paint a background scene on the paper. For example, if you are making a forest scene, you could draw trees and a waterfall on the paper. If you are making an underwater scene, you could paint fish, coral, and water on the paper. When your background design is finished, glue the paper to the inside back of your box.

Now start gluing things to the inside of the box. You can even hang things from the "ceiling" by using thread. Let's say you're creating a beach shadow box. Along the bottom you could spread some glue and then sprinkle sand on it. A small rock could be a boulder. A few twigs with some red crepe paper could be a campfire. A stick could be a log, and a marble could be a beach ball. Get the idea?

TRAVEL TRIVIA
Arkansas contains more mineral springs than any other state.
Mammoth Spring, one of the largest mineral springs in the world, produces 200 million gallons of water each day.

PEN PAL CLUB

Start your own pen pal club all across the country!

You Will Need: Small address book, pen, paper, computer or typewriter

Whenever you meet other kids on your trip and make friends, collect their names and addresses in a small address book. As soon as you get home, send them a short note on the back of a photo card (see #94) or on stationery.

Let them know that you will keep writing to them if they write back. If you both have computer E-mail addresses, it's even easier! If you're really pressed for time and have a lot of friends in your pen pal club, you can write a general note about what's been going on in your life and then make one photocopy for everybody. Leave some room at the bottom, though, to put a more personal message.

BE A JOURNALIST

Make a record of your family's vacation adventures by publishing your very own family newspaper.

You Will Need: Computer or typewriter, paper, tape, scissors, photographs from your trip

Interview your family. Ask them questions about their most favorite and least favorite parts of the trip. Write about fun things you learned and the people you met. When you have all your stories typed (or written) in columns about 2 inches wide, cut and tape them onto another sheet of paper so that it looks like a newspaper.

If you want to include parts of pictures from your trip, here's a way to do it without cutting up your photographs: Draw a box on the page where you want your photo to go. Cut out the box and carefully tape the photograph to the back of the paper so you can see the part of the picture you want through the hole.

Don't forget to give your newspaper a name, and put headlines on every story, just like a real newspaper. Make photocopies when you're done, and send them to your friends and relatives.

POSTCARD MOBILE

Postcard mobiles are a "moving" reminder of what you saw on your trip!

You Will Need: 5 to 10 postcards (the same size), string, scissors, 2 wire hangers, glue, tape, hole punch

Cut enough pieces of string or yarn so that you have 1 for every 2 postcards you will hang. Make them different lengths, but make sure that they are between 6 and 18 inches. Glue 2 postcards together, back to back, with a piece of string between them. Make the base for the mobile out of 2 wire hangers.

Hold the hangers together, like they would be in a closet. Tightly tape the top hooks together and then twist them at the neck so that the bottoms make a cross. When the postcards are dry, you can even cut them into simple shapes such as a circle, triangle, or square. Be careful not to cut the string!

Tie the end of each string to a different place on your mobile base. Now you can hang the mobile from a ceiling or doorway.

TIME CAPSULE SCRAPBOOK

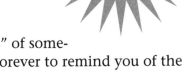

Save those memories, and they'll never fade away.

You Will Need: Paper, cardboard, tape or glue, items you want to save

A scrapbook is just what it sounds like—a book that is made up of the "scraps" of somebody's life. If you save things and put them into a scrapbook, you'll have them forever to remind you of the good times you've had.

You can put anything you want into your scrapbook—ticket stubs, napkins, brochures, photos, candy wrappers, found pennies, and so on. Add to it everytime you take a trip. Add little notes to yourself underneath each item as a reminder of what those special scraps mean.

STAMP IT

You probably know about rubber stamps. But did you know you can make stamps out of leaves, rocks, shells, and other natural objects?

You Will Need: Heavy paper, shallow plate, poster paint, newspaper, and things collected during your trip (leaves, rocks, shells, etc.)

Spread newspaper over your work area so that cleaning up will be easy, then pour some poster paint into a wide, shallow plate. You might want to experiment on a scrap piece of paper to see what your prints will look like before doing it for real.

Lightly dip one side of your object into the paint and then firmly press it onto the bottom half of your paper. Make sure that the paint isn't thick and drippy by holding the object over the tin until it stops dripping. When the paint is dry, fold your paper in half like a greeting card. Write notes on the inside for birthdays, holidays, or thank-yous.

If you use more than one color of paint, make sure that the first paint is dry before adding another color. Rinse your stamp off in water before using another color.

TRAVEL TRIVIA

The Mississippi River is the largest in North America, flowing from Minnesota's Lake Itasca to the Gulf of Mexico—a distance of approximately 2,350 miles. It is one of the busiest commercial waterways in the world.

THE ANSWERS

Chapter 2

35. Pigeon, pine cone, pizza, poodle, puddle.

36. Gas pump, igloo, surfboard, socks, wall clock.

37. Hammer, candle, eyeglasses.

42. Cow on ferris wheel, lawn mower, chair, frying pan, telephone.

43. Radio, ruler, rabbit, ring, rake.

44. Pencil, spoon, baseball bat.

45. Inline skates, mountain bike, laptop computer, Frisbee, payphone, streetlight, stop sign, car, televisions, basketball court

56. Rooster, robot, roller skate, radio, rake.

57. Person driving from the backseat, truck without tires, driver wearing helmet, car door opening the wrong way, bird wearing necklace.

58. E-N-E-R-G-Y

59. Giant toadstool, tire, hammer on counter, clothes iron, treasure chest.

60. Candle, clock, coffee pot, cup, cash register.

61. H-U-N-G-R-Y

62. There are 6: seagull, surfboard, sunscreen, sunglasses, sandals, and soda.

63. Tree in pool, fish in pool, air bubbles coming from man on diving board, lifeguard facing wrong way, surfboarder.

64. S-P-L-A-S-H

65. Women's shoes, mousetraps, single-striped croquet balls, mittens, nails.

66. Football and helmet, lightbulb and lamp, bowling ball and pin, baseball and bat, croquet mallet and ball (2 stripes).

69. All three signs in the top row have a match somewhere in the two rows below them. Sign A matches E, B matches I, and C matches H.

Chapter 6

202. DEER Class, Your T+CHAIR [teacher] can KNOT BEE at SCHOOL today. H+EAR [here] is your assignment. WRITE a STORE+Y [story] about a WHALE, a WALRUS, and a TIE+ger [tiger].

204. 1) INDIANA. 2) OREGON. 3) ALABAMA. 4) MISSISSIPPI. 5) CALIFORNIA.

6) TEXAS. 7) TENNESSEE. 8) MAINE. 9) VERMONT. 10) VIRGINIA. 11) OKLA-HOMA. 12) ARIZONA. 13) FLORIDA. 14) KENTUCKY. 15) GEORGIA. 16) CONNECTI-CUT. 17) IDAHO. 18) MONTANA. 19) NE-BRASKA. 20) ILLINOIS.

206. Pour the pitcher of water down the drain. Because the drain is clogged, the water will rise, bringing the Ping-Pong ball up with it.

210 A) TARP. B) GIGGLE. C) BRACE. D) LUCKY. Answer to riddle: GARBAGE TRUCK.

212. A) Wisconsin. B) New York. C) Texas. D) Idaho. E) Montana. F) Florida.

213. Puzzle 1: pit, fit, mat, sat, wet, get, tot, jot. Puzzle 2: pen, ten, fun, gun, ton, ion, can, fan.

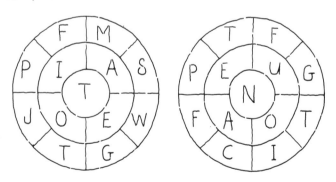

214. Matching pairs: A6 and D2, C4 and B1 and E5.

~housands of Y+EARS ago, BEE+4 [be-
~RIGERATORS and TV SETS were
~AVEMEN used CLUBS and

SPEARS to kill their prey. They cooked the STEAKS over a big FIRE.

216. Stack the encyclopedias so you can climb them and reach the key.

218. Instead of flying straight in, you'll have to angle the shuttle diagonally to make it through the doorway.

222. Fat cat, new zoo, night light, loud cloud, far car, free bee, tall ball.

223. Take the swan across the river first. Then go back and get the tiger. Drop the tiger off on the other side, but before you leave, pick up the swan again. Carry the swan back across the river, and drop it off. Pick up the cashews and carry them across the river. Then come back and get the swan.

226. The third pyramid from the left matches the original, except that it is shown from the side instead of from above.

228. Throw the baseball up to your friend. Because fishing line is much lighter than rope, you can throw it farther. When your friend catches the ball, have him use the fishing line to pull up the rope. Then he can tie it up to a rock and climb down.

230. 1) Adam. 2) Don. 3) Bill. 4) Charlie. 5). Theater.

231. Top row, left to right: stop, yield, one way, do not enter. Bottom row: railroad crossing, interstate route, U.S. route, state route.

232. From left to right, the kites in the air belong to Ray, Jean, Bill, and Lisa.

233. When explorers found KING Tut's GRAVE, they couldn't believe their EYES. They found a golden BOAT, a giant CAT made of marble, PLATES and CUPS made of WOOD, and more COINS and DIAMONDS than they could count.

235. Total number of boxes is 79.

236. Top row, left to right: lost & found, currency exchange, falling rocks, drinking water, no entry. Bottom row: gift shop, information, viewing area, Customs, hiking trail.

Chapter 7

237. 1) I. 2) J. 3) H. 4) G. 5) D. 6) F. 7) C. 8) E. 9) A. 10) B.

238. 1) C. 2) A. 3) D. 4) C. 5) A. 6) D.

241. 1) B. 2) B. 3) D. 4) C. 5) B. 6) A.

242. 1) C. 2) A. 3) B. 4) B. 5) A. 6) C.

243. Tiger: kitten, cow: calf, seal: whelp, horse: foal, kangaroo: joey, eagle: eaglet, goose: gosling, swan: cygnet, turkey: poult, deer: fawn, rooster: chick.

248. 1) A. 2) C. 3) D. 4) B. 5) D. 6) C.

250. Once upon a TIME, there was a young GIRL by the NAME of Goldilocks. But her FRIENDS called her GOLDY. One DAY while GOLDY was WALKING through the forest, a BIG, hairy brown BEAR jumped out from behind a TREE and said, "Didn't I CATCH you in my HOUSE last YEAR?"

"No!" said GOLDY. "I've never SEEN you before in my whole LIFE!"

"I THINK you're LYING," said the BEAR. "You CAME into my HOUSE and ate all my SOUP! Then you broke my favorite CHAIR! Then you went to SLEEP in my BED! I'd KNOW you anywhere!"

So GOLDY RAN away as FAST as she could and didn't LOOK BACK once.

252. 1) A. 2) A. 3) C. 4) D. 5) C. 6) D.

256. Surf, sand, ocean, pool, car, forest, tent, picnic, maps, drive, plane, ticket, museum, tour, truck, beach, swimming, campfire, hotel, holiday.

261. 1) D. 2) A. 3) C. 4) B. 5) A. 6) A.

262. 1) C. 2) I. 3) E. 4) G. 5) H. 6) B. 7) D. 8) J. 9) A. 10) F.

263. 1) G. 2) E. 3) I. 4) H. 5) A. 6) B. 7) C. 8) J. 9) F. 10) D.

267. 1) D. 2) C. 3) B. 4) C. 5) C. 6) D.

270. 1) their. 2) it's. 3) pair. 4) blew. 5) to. 6) threw. 7) bow. 8) rain. 9) plane. 10) bore.

271. 1) D. 2) A. 3) C. 4) C. 5) C. 6) B.

274. 1) Maryland. 2) South Carolina. 3) New Hampshire. 4) Indiana. 5) Mississippi.

6) Arkansas. 7) California. 8) Nevada. 9) North Dakota. 10) Utah.

275. Tommy plays a TUBA in the SCHOOL BAND. He loves to RIDE his MOUNTAIN BIKE and play SOCCER with his friends. His favorite FOOD is macaroni and CHEESE with a big helping of FRENCH FRIES. In the MORNING he delivers PAPERS and saves all his MONEY for a trip to NEW YORK City to see the WORLD TRADE Center. When he GROWS up, he wants to be a FIRE FIGHTER.

276. 1) E. 2) F. 3) C. 4) G. 5) H. 6) J. 7) I. 8) A. 9) D. 10) B.

277. 1) C. 2) A. 3) D. 4) A. 5) D. 6) C.

279. 1) F. 2) D. 3) G. 4) J. 5) I. 6) B. 7) H. 8) A. 9) C. 10) E.

283. 1) C. 2) A. 3) B. 4) A. 5) A. 6) C.

284. 1) dromedary. 2) crocodile. 3) African. 4) frog. 5) spider. 6) tortoises. 7) Trick question: They're all the same cat! 8) Indian. 9) American. 10) South American.

286. 1) I. 2) G. 3) A. 4) J. 5) E. 6) H. 7) B. 8) F. 9) C. 10) D.

287. Bang, pang, bald, plan, lag, bag, man, nag, nap, lap, gap, map, mad, lad, pad, lad, palm, dam.

288. The correct answer for all 6 questions is A.

290. 1) H. 2) J. 3) G. 4) A. 5) I. 6) B. 7) C. 8) D. 9) E. 10) F.

291. 1) G. 2) F. 3) A. 4) J. 5) I. 6) H. 7) D. 8) B. 9) E. 10) C.

292. Julius Johnson owns a small STORE on Maple STREET. He sells plates, DISHES, and cups, as well as KNIVES, forks, and SPOONS. His grandFATHER started the family business in a ONE-room building BACK in 1929. Now Julius SELLS lots of useful THINGS to eat with from all around the WORLD. Last week, he SOLD five hundred BOWLS made out of RUBBER that won't break if you DROP them on the floor. What will he THINK of next?

293. 1) A. 2) C. 3) D. 4) A. 5) B. 6) C.

Chapter 8

317. Top row, left to right: start the clock, stop the clock, traveling. Bottom row: stop the clock, score.

341. 1 = Nose on your Face; 2 = Eyes in your Head; 4 = Quarts in a Gallon; 6 = Strings on a Guitar; 9 = Planets in the Solar System; 12 = Days of Christmas; 12 = Eggs in a Dozen; 26 = Letters in the Alphabet; 36 = Inches in a Yard; 52 = Cards in a Deck; 100 = Years in a Century; 365 = Days in a Year; 5,280 = Feet in a Mile; 20,000 = Leagues under the Sea.

351. Top row, left to right: holding, interference. Bottom row: time out, safety, touchdown/field goal.

INDEX